John and Sally McKenna's "Bridgestone 100 Best" Guides give all the information you need to enjoy the best of Irish food. These restaurants are chosen for the quality of their cooking, their individuality, their creativity, and their value for money, each earning the right to call themselves one of the 100 Best.

The Bridgestone 100 Best Guides to Ireland are the most up-to-the-minute annual guides you can buy. Intensively and dedicatedly researched, with a wealth of detail and description of the chosen entries and written with humour and personal experience, these are the essential travelling companions. If you wish to find the very best of Ireland, you need to travel with John and Sally McKenna's Bridgestone Guides.

Readers' praise for the Bridgestone Guides:

"Your recommendations were outstanding . . . we can't wait to try more next year"
L. & M. G., Tallahassee

"We used your excellent guide for a tour of Ireland and found it invaluable . . . we shall certainly use the guide on our next visit".
N. & S. G. Bayswater

"Wonderfully, wonderfully helpful . . ."
K. R., Portsmouth

"I really enjoyed your in-depth views and graphic descriptions which I thought extremely accurate . . ."
M. M., London

GW00320474

First published in 1995 by
Estragon Press Ltd, Durrus, Bantry, Co Cork
© Estragon Press

Text copyright © John McKenna and Sally McKenna 1995
Illustrations and maps copyright © Ken Buggy 1995
Cover photo © Lucy Johnston 1995

The moral right of the authors has been asserted

ISBN 1 874076 14 6

Printed by Colour Books Ltd, Baldoyle, Co Dublin Tel: (01) 832 5812
Designed by Karl Tsigdinos/Graphic Design, Dublin Tel: (01) 2600 899
Typeset by Seton Music Graphics, Bantry, Co Cork Tel: (027) 50742
Cover Photo by Lucy Johnston, Garville Lane Studios Tel: (01) 496 0584

All rights reserved. No part of this publication may be reproduced,
stored in a retrieval system or transmitted in any form or by any
means, without the prior permission of the publishers.

Whilst every effort has been made to ensure that the information
given in this book is accurate, the publishers and authors do not
accept responsibility for any errors or omissions.

THE BRIDGESTONE 100 BEST RESTAURANTS IN IRELAND 1995

JOHN MCKENNA

SALLY MCKENNA

With illustrations by Ken Buggy

ESTRAGON PRESS

In memory of David Burns

With thanks to:

Des Collins, Karl, Lucy, Eddie, Elaine, Sarah Bates, Cynthia Harrison, Cathleen Buggy, Ray Buckley and John Harold, James O'Shea, Pat Ruane, Louis Lentin, Micky O'Neill, Ciaran Tanham, Pat Duffner, Maureen Daly, Caroline McGrath, Colette Tobin, Mary and Des Rainey.

John McKenna was born in Belfast and educated both there and in Dublin, where he practised as a barrister before turning to writing in 1989. His work appears in newspapers and magazines in Ireland and the U.K. He has won Glenfiddich Awards, as regional writer and for radio programmes, in 1993 and 1994.

Sally McKenna was born in Kenya, and brought up on the Pacific island of Fiji before coming to Ireland in 1982. She cooked professionally before turning to writing about food and restaurants.

Ken Buggy was born in Dublin in 1947 and has spent most of his working life abroad. He now lives in Kinsale with his wife Cathleen and their four children.

JOHN McKENNA and SALLY McKENNA won the first André Simon Special Commendation Award in 1992 for the second edition of The Bridgestone Irish Food Guide. The third edition of The Bridgestone Irish Food Guide was short-listed for a Glenfiddich Award in 1994.

The RTE television series "McKennas' Ireland" was written and presented by John and Sally McKenna and directed by Micky O'Neill. It was produced for Crescendo Concepts Ltd. by Louis Lentin.

ULSTER

NORTH CHANNEL

ATLANTIC OCEAN

LONDONDERRY

ANTRIM

BELFAST

DONEGAL

TYRONE

DOWN

FERMANAGH

ARMAGH

SLIGO

MONAGHAN

LEITRIM

CAVAN

LOUTH

MAYO

ROSCOMMON

MEATH

CONNACHT

LONGFORD

WESTMEATH

GALWAY

OFFALY

KILDARE

DUBLIN

DUBLIN

GALWAY

LEINSTER

LAOIS

WICKLOW

N
W — E
S

CLARE

CARLOW

KILKENNY

IRISH SEA

TIPPERARY

WEXFORD

LIMERICK

WATERFORD

KERRY

CORK

CORK

MAP SHOWS COUNTY DIVISIONS
AND PROVENCES.

0 ——— 40 ——— 80 KMS
0 ——— 25 ——— 50 MLS

MUNSTER

BRIDGESTONE

Contents

BRIDGESTONE

BRIDGESTONE IS JAPAN'S LARGEST tyre manufacturer and one of the top three in the world. Founded in 1931, the company has striven to maintain an emphasis on technological advancement and service while expanding the scale and scope of its operations. As a result the company is recognised as a leader in tyre manufacturing and technology.

Bridgestone tyres are presently sold in more than 150 countries. There are twelve manufacturing plants in Japan with others throughout the world including the U.S.A. and Australia. Bridgestone now also manufactures its tyres in Europe following the acquisition in 1988 of the Firestone Tyre and Rubber Company.

They manufacture tyres for many different vehicles, from trucks and buses to passenger cars and motor-cycles. Its commercial vehicle tyres enjoy a worldwide reputation for superior cost-per-kilometre performance, and its aircraft tyres are used by more than 100 international airlines. Many Japanese cars imported to Ireland arrive with Bridgestone tyres and a host of exotic sports cars including Ferrari, Lamborghini, Porsche, Jaguar and TVR are now fitted with Bridgestone tyres as original equipment.

Bridgestone is at the forefront of tyre research and development. Its proving ground in Kuroiso City, Japan covers 400,000 square metres and consists of a 3.5 kilometre banked test track and skid pan which together contain more than 40 different road surfaces. Bridgestone also operate an advanced R&D facility in Kodaira, Japan. Testing focuses on a wide range of features including directional stability, skid resistance, durability, abrasion resistance, riding comfort and noise reduction. All this data is then put to valuable use in the development of new and better tyres. Bridgestone is now the most technologically advanced tyre manufacturer in the world.

In June 1990 Bridgestone (Ireland) Ltd was established as a subsidiary of the multinational Bridgestone Corporation to take over the distribution of its tyres in Ireland. The company operates from its offices and warehouse in Tallaght in Dublin where it stocks a wide range of passenger car, commercial vehicle and earthmover tyres. Bridgestone staff also provide sales, technical and delivery services all over the country.

● *Bridgestone tyres are available from tyre dealers throughout Ireland. For further information contact Bridgestone (Ireland) Ltd., Unit A30, Greenhills Industrial Estate, Tallaght, Dublin 24. Tel: (01) 452 7766 Fax: (01) 452 7478*

How To Use This Book

THIS BOOK IS arranged alphabetically, firstly by virtue of County names — County Cavan is followed by County Clare which is followed by County Cork, and so on — and then within the counties the individual entries are arranged alphabetically — so Longueville House, in north Cork, will follow after Lettercollum House, which is in south west Cork. Entries in Northern Ireland are included in a separate section. The maps in the book are intended only as a general guide and we recommend that they be used in conjunction with an accurate Ordnance Survey map.

All visits to the restaurants, hotels, cafés and eateries included in this book were made anonymously. All meals were paid for and any offers of discounts or gifts were refused.

In cases where we felt the food served in a restaurant was of such a special, unique, stature, where the best Irish ingredients were presented in their finest possible state, we have marked the entry with a ★.

In cases where we felt the food served in a restaurant was of special interest we have marked the entry with a ➥, meaning that the entry is worthy of making a detour in order to enjoy the food.

In cases where we feel a restaurant offers excellent value for money, we have marked these entries with a £.

Whilst opening times are given for restaurants, it is always advisable to telephone in advance and check opening times when booking a meal. Note also that many restaurants in the south and the west of the country are seasonal, closing during the winter months, whilst others alter their opening hours out of season.

Prices: the prices quoted represent an average price for a meal for one person, without wine. Where a restaurant offers meals at a set price, this is the price we have quoted and, should you choose from the à la carte, you should expect to pay more.

All prices and details are correct at the time of going to press but, given the volatile nature of restaurants and the peripatetic nature of restaurant staff, we are unable to accept any responsibility should the circumstances of any of the entries change.

Finally, we greatly appreciate receiving reports, suggestions and criticisms from readers.

The Bridgestone Awards

STARRED RESTAURANTS ★

Assolas House, Kanturk, Co Cork
Ballymaloe House, Shanagarry, Co Cork
Clifford's, Cork City, Co Cork
Drimcong House, Moycullen, Co Galway
Dunworley Cottage, Butlerstown, Co Cork
Erriseaske House Hotel, Ballyconneely, Co Galway
Eugene's, Ballyedmond, Co Wexford
Lacken House, Kilkenny, Co Kilkenny
Longueville House, Mallow, Co Cork
The Oystercatcher, Oysterhaven, Co Cork
Roscoff, Belfast, Co Antrim
Truffles, Sligo, Co Sligo

RESTAURANTS WORTH A DETOUR ➡

Restaurant Patrick Guilbaud, Dublin, Co Dublin
Heir Island Restaurant, Heir Island, Co Cork
Ivory Tower Restaurant, Cork, Co Cork
Lettercollum House, Timoleague, Co Cork
Nick's Warehouse, Belfast, Co Antrim
Packies, Kenmare, Co Kerry
Quay House, Clifden, Co Galway
Roly's Bistro, Dublin, Co Dublin
Shank's, Bangor, Co Down
Shiro Japanese Dinner House, Ahakista, Co Cork
Tonlegee House, Athy, Co Kildare

RESTAURANTS WHICH OFFER
EXCELLENT VALUE FOR MONEY £

Drimcong House, Moycullen, Co Galway
Eugene's Restaurant, Ballyedmond, Co Wexford
Lettercollum House, Timoleague, Co Cork
Mainistir House, Kilronan, Aran Island, Co Galway
Packie's, Kenmare, Co Kerry
Roscoff, Belfast, Co Antrim
Shank's, Bangor, Co Down
Quay House, Clifden, Co Galway
Roly's Bistro, Dublin, Co Dublin

READY FOR THE RUSH

Introduction

IN IRELAND, we have a great fondness for fictions, a great fondness for imagining that things are as we wish them to be, rather than as they actually are. We have become conscious, in the last few years, of being somewhat guilty of contributing to this rather lovely way of living, this alliance of metaphor and metaphysics.

Ever since we began to write about Irish food, beginning in 1989 when we bought an ancient Renualt 4 for £100 and tootled off down the road, we have been talking about and writing about Ireland's "food culture". This is a rather grandiose phrase, suggesting as it does an inherent and instinctive love of, and appreciation and respect for, good food. The phrase also conveniently ties up the entire nation into one containable bundle, thus assisting a favourite fiction which appeals mightily to us: the idea that, despite our almost shocking diversities of character and temperament, that we are all brothers.

But if this idea of a food culture does have some truth, then how can we explain away the sort of situation which is likely to happen if you go to a shop in Donegal, let us say, or in County Limerick. You ask the assistant if they have coffee. She points you to the serried ranks of instant powders and what have you. You say: 'Actually, I wonder if you have any real coffee?'. The assistant points you to a shelf, stocked with Gold Blend. Oh dear.

Yet, in the area of West Cork where we are presently living, the plenitude of good food which can be found and enjoyed is thrilling and it is possible, if one surveys the entire county of Cork, to speak genuinely and seriously not just about a "food culture", but about an "Irish food culture".

Consider the matter of the Clonakilty Black Pudding. This is a simple food made by a splendid man called Edward Twomey, in the storybook village of Clonakilty. The Irish never lost a taste for blood puddings — indeed, one of the specialities of Cork city is a sheep's blood pudding called Drisheen, whose pungency makes even the strongest of stomachs nervous — but they regarded it as a marginal food, fit to be fried on Sunday morning and that was that.

Yet in the last decade, Mr Twomey's insistent, proud promotion of his pudding, made to an original Harrington family recipe which is more than a century old, has turned it into the most unlikely culinary cult food. You can find it in Michael Clifford's splendid restaurant in Cork city, served with blinis and a purée of local mushrooms. In Katherine Noren's Dunworley Cottage restaurant, just a few miles from Clonakilty itself, the pudding is served with a lingonberry sauce. In Timoleague, a couple of miles further, Con McLoughlin, in Lettercollum House, will pair Mr Twomey's creation with a red wine apple sauce.

The classic concoction, unlikely as it may sound, remains the invention of Gerry Galvin, a cook who gifted the village of Kinsale with its reputation for good food almost two decades ago, and who now cooks in Drimcong House, near Galway. Mr Galvin's recipe pairs the pudding with fried oysters and a confit of apple and onion, the dish finished by a mustard cream sauce.

Most decent chefs in this neck of the woods, and in necks further afield, now have an original recipe involving Mr Twomey's celebrated pudding. In a country where restaurant cooking has, until recently, been nothing more than a pale imitation of French cuisine, this little shock of creativity is valuable, but it is also a symbol of what has been slowly brewing amongst the good cooks, amongst the creative culinary imaginations.

Irish cooks, both professional and domestic, have, in recent years, come to realise that they are blessed with two vital gifts. Firstly, many of the basic foods found in Ireland are astonishingly pure in taste, untampered, true to their nature. Secondly, it is a simple matter for a cook to have an intimate dialogue with the food producing environment in their immediate locality: in Lettercollum House, they have an ancient walled garden; in Dunworley Cottage, the famous nettle soup is made from hand-gathered nettles, the smoked mussels from wild mussels; in Longueville House in north county Cork, they not only produce almost all the food they need, they also make a small amount of white wine each year and William O'Callaghan, the young cook, is about to begin a search for truffles on the estate.

If you visit the charmingly surreal Shiro Japanese Dinner House in Ahakista, then the mackerel which Kei Pilz prepares for sashimi will have been caught that morning by her husband. In Ballymaloe House, in East Cork, Myrtle Allen raises this idea of a food dialogue to a creed: ducks from Mrs Northridge, hand-made butter from Maucnaclea cheeses, porridge from Macroom which has been roasted by hand, fish from Ballycotton Bay, just down the road, meat from Mr Cuddihy's little butcher's shop in the village.

In west Cork, the dashing peninsulas can be described by name, but also according to the cheesemakers who live on them. On the Sheep's Head peninsula Jeffa Gill makes Durrus, a raw milk cheese in the tomme style, using morning milk and there are cheesemakers on both of the adjoining peninsulas — Veronica Steele makes Milleens on the Beara peninsula, Gabriel and Desmond are made by Bill Hogan on the Schull peninsula, where Giana Ferguson also makes Gubbeen cheese.

There are also cheesemakers to the north — Ardrahan, Carraig and Coolea — and to the east — Maucnaclea, Carrigaline. They are all cheeses which have borrowed their styles from foreign models — the English territorials, Dutch goudas, French and Swiss styles — but their individuality arises from the concentrated milk butterfat content which Irish pastures bequeath to the dairy farmers and cheesemakers.

This may seem to be a happy picture of a food culture at work but, in fact, this picture is simply a compass of individuals, determined and head-strong folk whose work echoes that of any type of creative artist. The obverse of this happy picture is the food culture which still dominates most peoples' lives in Ireland, the food culture which is systematic and mechanised, commercialised and export-obsessed, vigorous and wealthy, profit-fixated. Everything, indeed, which the artisans and cheesemakers and fish smokers are not.

You have to burrow below the commercial food culture in Ireland in order to find the real thing, to find those foods which are stamped with the personality of their producers. It is, in fact, possible to visit Ireland and to completely miss the foods we have mentioned here, possible to choose the wrong places to eat and stay and to never encounter foods which are as distinctive as any in the world. For one happy feature of the artisan foods, and the good restaurants, is that they are not just totally unclichéd, they are often completely unlikely.

Take, for example, an experience we enjoyed on the south east coast of Ireland some time back. At the end of a long day we pulled off the road at a place called Eugene's, in a small village called Ballyedmond, not far from Wexford town. This is a combination of pub, chipper and restaurant, the latter with much the same sort of decorative charm as a portakabin.

We ate sauté sea scallops, a salad with roasted beetroot, avocado and cherry tomatoes, then a splendid breast of chicken with creamy Puy lentils and a braised shank of lamb with caramelised root vegetables. We then had some local cheese, the wonderful Croghan, made near to the restaurant by Luc and Anne Van Kampen. Desserts were excellent home-made ice creams and a decent lemon tart. All the vegetables were grown organically, and culled from local producers, as were the fish and the meats. Dinner was so cheap we actually protested.

The Eugene of this eponymous restaurant is Eugene Callaghan, winner of the first Roux brothers' young chef of the year competition some years back and formerly right hand man to Paul Rankin in Roscoff, in Belfast, the restaurant which has consistently been home to the most exciting food in Ireland in recent years. He not only cooks in the restaurant, he also makes the lunches in the pub and even fries the fish in the chipper. It would be difficult to imagine a more unlikely place to find such a decisively talented cook, but here he is.

This is the sort of surprise, the sort of happy surprise, which you have to get used to when hunting down good food in Ireland. We have always included quite detailed instructions in our books as to how to find the various producers and cheesemakers we write about. Frequently these are tortuous in the extreme and, when we began to do it first, people, politely, doubted our sanity.

Yet, gradually, we have found more and more travellers making their way to the back of nowhere in order to buy some Durrus cheese, or to find some Ummera smoked salmon or maybe even meet Chris Jepson, a local fish smoker who is so reclusive that we have written about his fish in three different books but never managed to meet him, yet. People who would otherwise disdain bed and breakfast accommo-dation will return religiously to Ken Buggy's Old Presbytery in Kinsale, not just for its baleful comfort, but because they like the still-warm soda bread in the morning, or the shot of Bushmills whiskey to be poured on top of a steaming bowl of porridge.

Standards mean nothing in Ireland, and price does not determine quality. When you find good food here you will also find good people, the people who make the good food. Modest and hard-working, their talents unveil a small culture where concern and application go hand in hand, where their work painstakingly evokes their own character.

Mr Twomey's pudding. Mrs Noren's nettle soup. Mr Callaghan's shank of lamb. Ms Gill's Durrus cheese. One is always conscious, in writing about these people, of the fact that they sound slightly unreal, unlikely. But they are real, these Irish artisans, and perhaps their work does amount to a "food culture", an "Irish food culture". Perhaps, although they certainly sound like it, they are not one of our fictions, after all.

JOHN MCKENNA
SALLY MCKENNA
Durrus, County Cork, 1995

THE LORD BAGENAL INN
Leighlinbridge, County Carlow Tel: (0503) 21668
James Kehoe

The wine list in The Lord Bagenal, which may be the restaurant's greatest claim to fame, is a magnificent piece of work, a tender exposition of great wines described in splendidly commonsense language.

"First and foremost, wine is made to be enjoyed" writes James Kehoe, the master.nind proprietor behind the list. "If we follow the traditionalists, we will not drink white wine with red meat, nor rosé with fish. I say you drink what you like, and that is what is important, what you like".

This is what is important about Mr Kehoe's splendid wine list, and his splendid restaurant. The list is not a bland recital of vintages and varietals, but is instead a careful canvas of fine wines, with the essentials of pleasure and accessibility underpining the reason why each bottle is on the list.

Truth be told, the greatest of Mr Kehoe's achievements is not just his wine list, but the fact that such a spiffing piece of work is put to play in the friendly, sociable and enjoyable bar and restaurant which is The Lord Bagenal Inn. They play classical music, hang splendid paintings by Irish artists on the walls, have linen table-cloths and good big glasses, but none of this is the slightest bit arch or reserved. The pleasure principle is what makes this place special, that and the fact that the enthusiasms which made Mr Kehoe go into the restaurant business when he was fifteen years old have never dimmed.

So, do make a feature of enjoying different wines with the food: La Ina and Marquesa de Real Tesoro sherries are perfect with lunchtime starters of crab meat in filo pastry, and Parma ham and salami with a fig and balsamic vinegar sauce. With main courses — deep-fried lemon sole, baked cod florentine — try the nuggety red Salice Salentino, from Puglia, way way down in the heel of Italy. The wines and the food were made for each other, and in the happy embrace of the dining room one will be smitten by the delights of this caring, sharing, quaffing place.

Open 12.30pm-2.15pm Mon-Sun, 6pm-10.30pm Mon-Sat, 6pm-9pm Sun
Closed Xmas and Good Fri
Average Price: lunch £9.50, bar lunch £5, dinner £18.95
Credit Cards: Visa, Access/Mastercard
No Service Charge
Full Licence
Wheelchair Access (happy to help)
Children — high chairs, lunch £5.50
Vegetarian menu always available
The Lord Bagenal Inn is signposted from the N9 Dublin/Carlow/Waterford road, a few miles south of Carlow town.

MACNEAN BISTRO
Blacklion, Co Cavan Tel: (072) 53022
Vera and Neven Maguire

Neven Maguire's culinary star is in the ascendent. This demure, boyish young man has been knocking the socks off the locals of Blacklion for some time now. But, with his success in the Young Chef of the Year competition in 1994, the word about this stellar young talent is moving abroad.

The restaurant is little more than a small front room on the main street in Blacklion. The cooking is shared by Vera and Neven, mother and son. There are two menus, an à la carte and the "chef's special", and it is to the latter that you are urgently directed. The "chef's special" is the responsibility of Maguire Jnr., a cook who, according to Mr Maguire Snr. "goes to bed with cookery books".

Game and beef dominate the menu, with fish correctly restricted to what can be bought fresh, and this can result in a simple dish of roasted cod in a red wine sauce which is to die for. For the sake of business, there must be straightforward things such as steak and potato gratin, but it is with signature dishes such as pan fried lamb with black pudding mousse, where eyes of lamb fillet are sealed with the mousse and served with pickles and minuscule vegetables, that we see the direction of a young chef in firm control of his skills. This year Neven has introduced a series of exotics to the menu: Kangaroo ("lovely" says Joe Maguire, Neven's father); Bison (a type of buffalo, no fat and a strong flavour), Ostrich fillet and Alligator (which tastes a bit like pork). The meat comes from Amsterdam, from a supplier whom they consider to be able to give them the most consistent quality.

But it is in the desserts that Mr Maguire's skills are best exemplified. A chocolate plate collection of white, milk and dark chocolate confections is exquisitely beautiful, whilst nougat ice-cream wears a Philip Tracey hat of spun sugar. You leave the restaurant on a veritable high, the narcotic delirium of these desserts coursing through your veins.

Open 5.30pm-9pm Tue-Sat, 12.30pm-9pm Sun
Closed Xmas (will always open for parties over 10)
Average Price: dinner £18.90, Sun lunch from £10
Credit Cards: Visa, Access/Mastercard
No Service Charge
Wine Licence
No Wheelchair Access
Children — welcome early evening only, high chairs
Vegetarian food always available
On the main street in Blacklion.

BARRTRA SEAFOOD RESTAURANT

Lahinch, Co Clare Tel: (065) 81280
Paul & Theresa O'Brien

They are clever restaurateurs, Paul and Theresa O'Brien. In the offshoot of their house which is the little collection of tables known as the Barrtrá Seafood Restaurant, overlooking the peaceful and endearing calm of Liscannor Bay, the menu is a clever reflection of both their culinary strengths and their culinary experiments.

Their strengths lie with the eternal verities: good breads; good soups; good fish and shellfish dishes which do little more than seal the perfect flavour of a perfectly fresh piece of fish or — one of their specialities — fresh lobster.

The experiment has begun to creep in in recent times — Oysters, home-smoked salmon, a greater array of dishes for vegetarians — smudgy home-made rolls and local Kilshanny cheeses make up the rest of this simple, just-right menu, a perfect holiday-time place with the intelligence to play to its strengths and to keep things simple and satisfying.

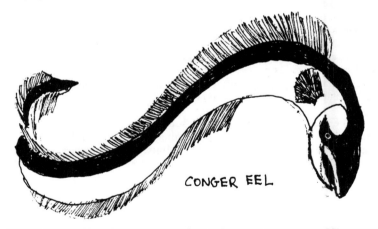

CONGER EEL

Open 12.30pm-2.30pm Mon-Sun, 6pm-10pm Mon-Sat
Closed weekdays off season, Jan-17 Mar
Average Price: dinner £16-£19, Sun lunch £9.50, weekday lunch £2-£10
Credit Cards: Visa, Access/Mastercard, Amex, Diners
No Service Charge
Wine Licence
Limited Wheelchair Access
Children — welcome early evenings
Recommended for Vegetarians
Signposted from the Lahinch-Milltown Malbay Road.

CAHERBOLANE FARMHOUSE

Corofin, Co Clare Tel: (065) 37638
Patricia Cahill

"Everything was perfection".

If we had a ten pound note for everytime we have heard this tribute paid to the Cahill family's Caherbolane Farmhouse, then our bank account might be able to shake off a condition which is so tortured it could get a gig in a Quentin Tarantino movie.

People speak in superlatives about Caherbolane, about the simple perfection of a cup of coffee, the perfection of the grilled and roasted meats — they have a cousin who is a butcher, clever people — the perfection of the hospitality. We have already told, in these pages, the extraordinary story of how, after cooking a superlative supper for us one evening, Patricia Cahill went home, then went into hospital and gave birth that night to a bouncing baby boy, David.

Extraordinary, of course, and it would be hard to top a story like that. Except it can be done. More recently, Patricia, after cooking dinner for six people, went home, then went into hospital and gave birth to a bouncing baby girl, Katie.

It is this sort of sang-froid, this effortless capacity to cope, which makes Caherbolane work. The energy and good cheer of the Cahills is addictive, their calmness is remarkable, and Patricia Cahill's cooking is sublime: linguine is served with gorgonzola and toasted nuts, smoked salmon parcels perfectly paired with a cream, ginger and chive sauce, rack of lamb blessed with a walnut crust and served with a pear bourbon sauce.

The fact, also, that one can find such terrific cooking in an area of Clare which is largely bereft of good eating houses, makes this a perfect base from which to scoot around the county, and somewhere to hurry home to for dinner, licking your lips all the way.

Open 7.30pm-9.30pm Mon-Sun
Closed Nov-Easter
Average Price: dinner £14
No Credit Cards
No Service Charge
No Licence (bring your own wine)
No Wheelchair Access
Children — welcome
Look for the signpost three miles outside Corofin on the road to Gort.

"WHEN YOUR HERE FOURTEEN YEARS — THATS' WHEN YOU CAN COOK .... MR COMMIS CHEF."

MACCLOSKEY'S

Bunratty House Mews, Bunratty, Co Clare Tel: (061) 364082
Gerry MacCloskey

Surrounded as they are in Bunratty by the ersatz and the fake side of Irish tourism, by the artificial and the laughable side of Irish food, the fact that the orientation of MacCloskey's is devoted, professional and real makes it even more valuable than if the restaurant was located elsewhere.

So if you find, on a visit to this touristic heartland, that the schlocky side of Irish travel and food culture is threatening to suffocate you, then do no more than walk down the steps into MacCloskey's, and you will be able to come up for air.

The MacCloskey five-course banquets, given every night in this restored basement restaurant, are the antithesis to those ladled out in nearby castles and keeps. Where the other banquets in Bunratty are tired and clichéd, the MacCloskey banquets wear their age well, and signature dishes such as mussels in still champagne, chicken in vermouth and warmed raspberries in a chocolate sauce are individual, clever things with true flavours. The initiation in the business of son Mark should add even greater fire to MacCloskey's professionalism.

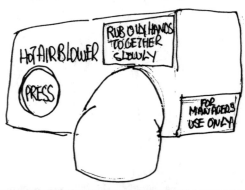

Open 7pm-10pm Tue-Sat
Closed Xmas-end Jan
Average Price: dinner £26
Credit Cards: Visa, Access/Mastercard, Amex, Diners
10% Service Charge
Full Licence
No Wheelchair Access
Children — no facilities
Vegetarian meals with prior notice
Take the N18 from Limerick and the restaurant is signposted in Bunratty.

SHEEDY'S SPA VIEW HOTEL

Lisdoonvarna, Co Clare Tel: (065) 74026 Fax: 74555
Frank & Patsy Sheedy

Sheedy's Spa View Hotel may look, initially, like just another paid-up member of that multitude of time-warped places to stay which one finds in the town of Lisdoonvarna, places built to cash in on the rage for matchmaking and resort holidays that made the reputation of this uninspiring town decades ago.

You walk inside and the décor is, of course, unsurprisingly unsurprising. You may even see those fabulous old ladies whom you more-than-half expected to find in a fading spa town like Lisdoonvarna, sitting just where you expected to find them, complete with dialogue courtesy of Alan Bennett . "That's lovely that, isn't it?", one old darling says to her lady companion.

The companion replies with silence.

"What is it?", asks the first.

But if there seems to be nothing else new, the surprise of Sheedy's comes, when you sit down to dinner. Sheedy's is different, because Frankie Sheedy cooks proper food, real food, not the sort of freezer-to-microwave-to-table food which you would normally expect to find in an hotel in a drowsy spa town. The expansiveness of the dinner menu may be initially off-putting, but the care which this kitchen shows, and the solecisms of the terrific staff, make dinner in Sheedy's a treat, especially since the somewhat dark décor of the dining room has been lightened.

The only problem, then, lies in making up your mind. Confit of duckling in a puff pastry case with a braised lettuce and green peppercorn sauce? Fillet of beef on a straw potato cake? Burren lamb with a mustard crust? Aran salmon on a vegetable spaghetti with a saffron sauce? As you can tell, this is a kitchen that is not happy until the maximum number of whirls and twirls have been visited on a plate, but their execution matches their ambition. Desserts are excellent, but don't miss the fine local Kilshanny cheese: indeed, it is always a good bet in Sheedy's to stay as close to the local foods — black pudding, west coast meats, fresh herb dishes — as possible.

Open 6.30pm-9pm Mon-Sun
Closed Nov-1 April (open New Year)
Average Price: dinner £12.50-£25
Credit Cards: Visa, Access/Mastercard, Amex, Diners
No Service Charge
Full Pub Licence
Wheelchair Access (to restaurant and gents toilet)
Children — welcome
Vegetarian dishes always offered
Lisdoonvarna town centre.

ADELE'S

Main Street, Schull, Co Cork Tel: (028) 28459
Simon Conner

The simplicity of the dishes which Simon Conner prepares in Adèle's —
poached salmon with a black pepper vinaigrette on mung bean sprouts;
spaghetti with parsley pesto, or that spaghetti served with peppers and
mushrooms; tagliatelle in an anchovy cream; angel hair pasta with
mussels in a spicy tomato sauce; pappardelle with chicken liver and
marjoram — doesn't hint at the increasing confidence with which he has
begun to cook.

Ever since he and Ferdia O'Dowd opened Adèle's up for night time
eaters — it has long been one of the essential staples of Schull, renowned
for its breads and cakes, its pies and pasties — they have simply got
better and better at the happy business of cooking good food.

Mr Conner has the considerable benefit of being self-taught, so
there is no nonsensical strait-jacket of technique tying down his imagination. He manages to prepare correct food which never concedes a
complexity of flavours: it looks simple, but the tastes are involved, and
thereby involving. Something like tagliatelle with anchovy cream will
manage to be rich, sinuous, intense, satisfying, inspired, and yet the
ingredients could not be more obvious.

A richer dish, such as fettucine with Dublin Bay prawns with a
tomato and caper butter, is gloriously achieved, whilst the angel hair
pasta accompanying pollo tonnato will have been wisely cooked in some
of the stock from the chicken. Small touches, but clever ones.

The teaming of everything, from pasta to sauce, from dish to
dressing, from beat-box atmosphere to hip-hop staff, from rare French
country wines to spectacular Italian specialities, is splendidly appropriate.
Adèle's is a carefree, romantic, youthful space, somewhere you come to
enjoy yourself. And, by heck, do you enjoy yourself.

Open 9.30am-10.30pm Mon-Sun (check out of season)
Closed Nov-Apr (open three weeks at Xmas)
Average Price: dinner £8-£15
No Credit Cards
10% Service Charge for parties of six or more
Wine Licence
Wheelchair Access, but not to toilets
Children — high chairs and half portions
Vegetarian options always available
At the top of the hill on Main Street in Schull.

AHERNE'S SEAFOOD BAR
163 North Main Street, Youghal, Co Cork Tel: (024) 92424 Fax: 93633
The Fitzgibbon family

There is a happy sense of timelessness about Aherne's.

That timelessness may be created by the fact that it is currently the third generation of Fitzgibbons who run this handsome place. But it may, equally, be the true sense of professionalism and a seriousness of purpose which the family espouse and practice, which makes the place ever-enduring.

This seriousness of purpose manifests itself as a determination to do things properly. This applies whether that is with the simple food cooked in the bar — you must try that mighty dish where smoked salmon and potatoes are gratinéed together, not to mention the great prawns in garlic butter and their fabulous seafood chowder — or in the cloistering, plump enfolds of the dining room, when David Fitzgibbon's fish cookery is given free and full rein — pan-fried scallops, monkfish and prawns in a coral sauce; Youghal Bay lobster thermidor; poached brill and prawns in Chablis; grilled sole on the bone.

This is very classic fish cooking, of course, and Aherne's follows a strict culinary code: If it ain't broke, don't fix it. The fish and shellfish dishes arrive with the classic accompaniments ever on hand, and they carry a near-certain rate of success.

Indeed, a success in Aherne's may gift you with some of the finest fish cooking it is possible to enjoy anywhere in the world, and you will go away and find that you, like so many others before you, have turned into a Cod Bore, or a Brill Bore, anxious to tell all and sundry about that fabulous fillet you enjoyed, that soulful shellfish which knocked you sideways, anxious to get the chance to explain to someone how bewitching it was. Sure, just wait 'till you tell them, they won't believe it . . .

Open 6.30pm-9.30pm Mon-Sun (bar meals 11am-10pm Mon-Sun)
Closed Xmas week
Average Price: dinner £23, (bar meals from £5)
Credit Cards: Visa, Access/Mastercard
10% Service Charge
Full Pub Licence
Wheelchair Access (incl disabled toilet)
Children — welcome
Vegetarian dishes available with notice
At the Waterford end of Youghal town, and well signposted.

ANNIE'S

Main Street , Ballydehob, Co Cork Tel: (028) 37292
Dano and Annie Barry

Annie Barry has the bestest, nicest, manner of any restaurant owner in the country. Her pacific nature with kids is legendary — Mrs Barry herself, of course, is too modest to agree with this — but she works her spell on adult kids with the same surreptitious ease, and quickly has you boggle-eyed and goo-goo with anticipation for the treat that is dinner in Annie's.

The restaurant is just a single room, with tables in multiples of pairs, nice and bright in summertime if you choose an early evening dinner, with drinks across the road in Levis's pub while you choose from the menu before Annie comes over to fetch you. Mr Barry doesn't try to do too much — and doesn't need to do too much — to coax the very best from his good ingredients.

The most preparation a piece of **Sally Barnes's** super smoked salmon ever needs is a squidge of lemon; with scallops as big and fat and coral-clawed as the ones you find in here, then a cream and white wine sauce may almost seem superfluous, but the sauce will be generous and precise, as generous and precise as an apricot sauce around a piece of finely roasted duck. The cooking may be light in execution, but it is deep in savour.

Right down to the very simple things — some luscious boiled spuds which you gobble up with the appetite of someone who has been hacking turf all day long, some baked cod or maybe — this is the regular's choice — a super-duper steak and some fab chips — Annie's gets it right. The temperament of this little place never changes, and never needs to, for who would tamper with a classic?

Open 6.30pm-9.30pm Tue-Sat (dinner only off season)
Closed Xmas, Oct and bank holidays (always check opening times off season)
Average Price: dinner £22
Credit Cards: Visa, Access/Mastercard
No Service Charge
Wine Licence
Wheelchair Access to restaurant but not to toilets
Children — welcome, but no facilities
Recommended for Vegetarians, with notice
In the centre of Ballydehob, across from Levis's pub.

ARBUTUS LODGE

Montenotte, Cork city, Co Cork Tel: (021) 501237 Fax: 502893
Michael & Declan Ryan

Whilst recent years have seen a greater informality make its way into the serving of food in Arbutus Lodge — nowadays, one of the biggest attractions of the hotel is the very modern, delicious dishes served in the bar at lunchtime — this is still an hotel with grandness written all over it.

The luxurious paintings signal the elevated manner of the place, and the glorious views out across Cork city add to the aristocratic ambience, the separateness, of Arbutus.

Whilst the lunchtime food in the bar is relatively simple, it always reveals the Ryan family's continuing interest and absorption in the latest food fashions and trends. As you would expect, the cooking is always executed with a professionalism that is the hallmark of this handsome and enduring operation.

Whilst the bar food is just as suitable as the more formal cooking of the dining room when it comes to matching a good bottle of wine from the extraordinary wine list to accompany it, one may want to wander into the more complex dishes which Helen Ward prepares in the restaurant to truly do justice to this most magisterial list. As comprehensive as an Oxford Companion, the Arbutus wine list is one of the very finest to be found in Ireland, and requires about twenty minutes of devoted study before you can even begin to make up your mind. The list continues to attract plaudits and awards every year, and it deserves each and every one of them.

Open 1pm-2pm, 7pm-9.30pm Mon-Sat
Closed Xmas
Average Price: lunch £12.50, dinner £22.50
Credit Cards: Visa, Access/Mastercard, Amex, Diners
No Service Charge
Full Licence
Wheelchair Access
Children — high chairs and half portions
Vegetarian dishes always available
Cork city centre, signposted from the Cork-Dublin road.

ASSOLAS COUNTRY HOUSE ★
Kanturk, Co Cork Tel: (029) 50015 Fax: (029) 50795
Joe and Hazel Bourke

That fine food writer, Annie Bell, last year wrote of the cooking in Assolas House, that "It is the absence of vanity in Hazel Bourke's cooking that makes it special: her 'dare to be simple' approach allows ingredients to speak for themselves".

No one has better described the work of this modest and most singular cook, and it is that aphoristic phrase "absence of vanity", which is the keynote. Hazel Bourke's food is confoundedly simple, and devastatingly delicious, so much so that if you were forced to find a single cook whose skill in the kitchen summons forth those flavours and tastes which one thinks of as quintessentially Irish, it is likely that it would be Mrs Bourke who would be summoned to summon forth those flavours.

She achieves this largely because she totally avoids the confections and artifices which seduce so many chefs. You can stay here for a week, and there will not be a single thing which you will eat which will overreach either itself, or the abilities of the kitchen.

Dinner menus from a few days in the middle of summer included dishes such as grilled black sole on the bone with garden herbs; fillet of brill baked in a wild mushroom crust on a delicate mustard sauce; grain-fed pigeon in red wine sauce; cream of garden peapod soup with croûtons, twice-baked Ardrahan cheese soufflé; oyster soup.

None of these dishes are new, but in Mrs Bourke's hands they are born anew each night. "Cooking? That's when things taste of themselves", wrote the great food sage Curnonsky. No one, but no one, is better at unravelling and unveiling the natural tastes of foods than Hazel Bourke.

And no one is better at orchestrating the service of these dishes than Joe Bourke, and nowhere is as nice a place in which to enjoy these dishes than Assolas. Be careful however: for there may be moments here of such utter bliss, that you will feel you shall surely expire from pleasure.

Open 7pm-8.30pm Mon-Sun (non-residents booking essential)
Closed Nov-mid March
Average Price: dinner £28
Credit Cards: Visa, Access/Mastercard, Amex
No Service Charge (tipping not expected)
Full Licence
Wheelchair Access to restaurant but not toilets
Children — welcome
Vegetarian meals with prior notice
On the Mallow to Killarney road, follow signs to Kanturk. Four-and-a-half miles before Kanturk you will see signs for Assolas House.

BALLYMALOE HOUSE ★

Shanagarry, Midleton, Co Cork Tel: (021) 652531 Fax: 652021
Ivan and Myrtle Allen

Myrtle Allen's philosophy of food in Ballymaloe House is durable, homespun, simple.

First, a country house hotel must encourage a circle of producers around and about you to produce the best foods they can, and you must support them as best you can. Keep everything local and, thereby, enjoy the benefit of foods which express themselves in terms of the micro-climate in which they are produced and reared.

Secondly, try to be as self-sufficient as you can: grow your own spuds, make your own chutneys, produce as much of the food you need through your own endeavours.

Then, when it comes to the cooking of this food, do it from scratch, and do it with ingredients as pristinely fresh as possible. No egotism must blunt the edge of the cooking: you just allow the food to speak of and for itself.

Then, when it comes to serving the food, do it simply, but courteously and as graciously as you can, with easy, spontaneous dialogue between customer, waiting staff and cook, a culinary conversation.

This is a simple modus operandi, a startlingly obvious one, and Myrtle Allen has never lost sight of this creed of simplicity, this respect for plainness in thinking and cooking, in twenty five years. During that time, the philosophy of Ballymaloe has remained consistent: respect for the fruits of the land, air and sea. Respect for the long-held culinary codes which best transform these fruits. Respect for the person who will enjoy the fruits of the cook's labours and, just as important, respect demanded for the efforts of the cook.

Many people find it difficult to see this simplicity at work. But there are many, still, who see in the Ballymaloe philosophy a logical, conscientious, organic way of working with the world. For them it is this deep thread, just as much as the delicious presentations on a plate which you will remember for years afterwards, which makes Ballymaloe special.

Open 12.30pm-1.30pm, 7pm-10pm Mon-Sun
Closed Xmas
Average Price: lunch from £10, dinner £30
Credit Cards: Visa, Access/Mastercard, Amex, Diners
No Service Charge
Full Licence
Wheelchair Access to restaurant but not easily to toilets
Children — high chairs, half portions for under 9yrs
Recommended for Vegetarians
Ballymaloe House is signposted from the N25 Cork-Waterford road, between Midleton and Castlemartyr, and in Midleton.

LA BIGOUDENNE

28 McCurtain Street, Fermoy, Co Cork Tel: (025) 32832
Rodolphe and Noelle Semeria

Rodolphe and Noelle Smeria's La Bigoudenne restaurant is as proto-typically French as the ceremonial, luridly-phallic, sharp-pointed hat which gives the restaurant its name.

During the day it is a simple café, with splendid food that perfectly restores the traveller: filled baguettes, chunky pâtés, home-made soups. A good on-the-road place, just as you would expect to find in France.

The speciality of the restaurant, and one that makes it worth travel-ling any distance to try, are the crêpes: the savoury ones — filled with ham and egg, egg and cheese, chicken and mushroom with cream, salad and blue cheese; and the sweet ones — filled with stewed apple, choco-late, pear and ice-cream. They are splendid on-the-road food, giving energy, brightening the soul.

At night, La Bigoudenne is transformed. The napery is brought out, and everything changes, with that seamless, easy French poise, to a more formal setting. For dinner, then, perhaps a glass of kir to begin, then a well envisioned dish of veal with some ceps, or fine fresh river trout or, one of their specialities, sweet fresh lobster with butter.

The food, the techniques and the styling come straight from northern France, and they create simple, enjoyable, calm tastes and a confident, almost serene atmosphere. In this neck of the woods, where there are all-too-few restaurants, La Bigoudenne is a vital asset, a fact which its devoted, faithful — and considerable — clientele attest to.

Open 12.30pm-5.30pm, 7pm-10pm Tue-Sat
Open all year incl Xmas
Average Price: lunch £5-£6, dinner £14.50
Credit Cards: Visa, Access/Mastercard
No Service Charge
Wine Licence
Wheelchair Access
Children — welcome, but no special facilities
Vegetarian options available on the day-time menu
On the main street in Fermoy.

BLAIR'S COVE RESTAURANT

Durrus, Co Cork Tel: (027) 61127
Philippe & Sabine De Mey

Dinner in Blair's Cove is centred around twin monuments. Firstly, the monumental selection of hors d'oeuvres, whose table is the centrepiece of this elegant, vaulted dining room.

Secondly, the monumental wood fire grill, from which the smoky smell of cooking meats is one of the most seductive features of this venerable restaurant.

You begin by plundering the array of hors d'oeuvres, choosing a selection of butter-crusted pâtés, maybe some sweet and some sour marinated herrings, maybe a pair of gigas oysters or a slice or two of smoked salmon, a little fresh crab meat with some mayonnaise, maybe a clean soupçon of pickled vegetables.

And whilst it is the simply-grilled meats which are the centrepiece of main courses, there are other more modern and well-tuned choices: recently, a loin of venison served with a venison sausage was superb; some chicken with guacamole was just right, and a slightly under-grilled fillet of tuna just heavenly.

Stated as simply as this, one can see how easy it is to have a crackingly fine evening in the 'Cove. Finish dinner with a hungry raid on the great local cheeses from Durrus or Gubbeen with crisp cumin biscuits, then cap it all with some well-made chocolate mousse, and it is all too nice. In the vaguely gothic ambience, the vaguely gothic roasts, grills, pickles and puddings are just right. Philippe De Mey orchestrates the dining room with an understated manner, some might even say a little offhand.

Open 7.30pm-9.30pm Tue-Sat (open Mon, Jul and Aug)
Closed Nov-mid Mar
Average Price: dinner £23
Credit Cards: Visa, Access/Mastercard, Amex, Diners
10% Service Charge
Restaurant Licence
Wheelchair Access to restaurant but not to toilets
Children — high chairs and half portions
One Vegetarian main course served each evening
One-and-a-half miles from Durrus on the Durrus-Goleen/Barleycove road: look for the gateway on the right-hand side.

CHEZ YOUEN
Baltimore, Co Cork Tel: (028) 20136
Youen Jacob

It is in the luxurious, classical, educated richness of his sauces that we can locate Youen Jacob's easy, expert affinity with his craft.

An emulsion of pristine, slurpy mayonnaise in which to dunk your shellfish platter. A hollandaise of angelic lightness under a fillet of salmon. Cream with green peppercorns for roasted beef. With each dish, through the course of a dinner in Chez Youen, the sauce is as essential as the principal ingredient.

Indeed, with fish and shellfish, it can seem that the sauce is truly the star, the real performer on a stage otherwise set by the fish. It is simple food, classic French food, and it is perfectly done. At lunchtime the fish and shellfish and sauces marry so well with a bottle of Muscadet, the richness of one counterpointed by the mineral sharpness of the other, that you might just forget that there is any work to be done in the rest of the day. When you get around to eating some tarte tatin, the best tarte tatin in your life, you wish the crumbly, intensity could last forever.

The music is always good, contributing to the hedonistic vitality of the restaurant, the atmosphere agreeably unpretentiousness, and there is great, great fun to be had.

Open noon-2.30pm, 6.30pm-10.30pm
Closed Sept-Easter (open for a period around Dec and Jan)
Average Price: lunch £12.50-£28, dinner £21-£35
Credit Cards: Visa, Access/Mastercard, Amex, Diners
No Service Charge
Wine Licence
Wheelchair Access (1 step to restaurant, no access to toilet)
Children — welcome
Vegetarian meals with prior notice
In centre of Baltimore village, overlooking the bay.

CLIFFORD'S ★

18 Dyke Parade, Cork, Co Cork Tel: (021) 275333
Michael and Deirdre Clifford

Although he is an exceptionally shy and reserved man, there is a thoroughly unreserved and lush savouring for food, and for the creativity of cooking, pulsing through Michael Clifford's veins.

"I scoffed the semolina and even the tapioca, but my favourite treat then was toast cut thick and spread with good beef dripping. The jellied meat juices seeped through into the soft centre and liquified pleasantly against the tongue: to this day I am ready to put in a good word for my favourite". These words, from his first book of recipes are the measure of the man, and the measure of his food: deliciousness, at all costs.

His cooking strikes an original and exquisite balance between competing disciplines: whilst it is sumptuous and comforting, it is based on relatively simple ingredients; his work is cosmopolitan, yet never happiest than when working with something grown and produced as close to the restaurant as possible. His food is modern in style and technique, but he can manage to evoke a taste that seems age-old and yet — and this is vital — he avoids any sense of that dread nostalgia which so restricts Irish cuisine.

His improvisations with Edward Twomey's Clonakilty Black Pudding includes one dish where the pudding meets with blinis and a purée of mushrooms, and another which intriguingly marries pudding, a poached egg, cabbage and smoked kassler. His inventiveness never rests: breast of wood pigeon with glazed celeriac in its own juices; grilled scallops with an aubergine mousse; fillet of beef with braised salsify and a rich Fleurie sauce.

Indeed, all of Mr Clifford's cooking, it seems, returns to that boyhood memory: warm, tactile tastes which melt and liquify, which sustain and delight. This romance with the whole business of cooking and running a restaurant makes Clifford's one of the most enjoyable places to eat in Ireland, for his staff are hopelessly happy in their work, and Michael's wife Deirdre augments the chef's shyness with her bubbly confidence.

Open 12.30pm-2.30pm, 7pm-10.30pm Tue-Sat
Closed Xmas Day and bank holidays
Average Price: lunch £13.95, dinner £29.50
Credit Cards: Visa, Access/Master, Amex, Diners
No Service Charge
Full Licence
No Wheelchair Access
Children — welcome, but no facilities
Special Vegetarian menu composed with prior discussion, £19
Clifford's is a minute's walk from Jury's Hotel: turn left, then right and at the first set of traffic lights you will see the restaurant on the corner.

LA COQUILLE

Main Street, Schull, Co Cork Tel: (028) 28642
Jean-Michel Cahier

Both the menu and the wine list in Jean-Michel Cahier's restaurant, at the lower end of Main Street in the lovely village of Schull, are stubbornly mute and uninformative, reminiscent of that somewhat arrogant French way of doing things. Scallops with garlic butter. Smoked salmon. Monkfish with green and red peppers. Rack of lamb with tarragon sauce. Fillet of steak with pepper sauce. Tarte tatin. Ice-cream.

This lack of elaboration does not hide an arrogant style when it comes to M. Cahier and M. Cahier's cooking, however: indeed, in more than one way, it suits his style of doing things. For his cooking is, effectively, just as he describes it: unencumbered by needless elaboration, choosing little more than classical pairings and time-honoured collaborations, the confidence to keep things simple.

With shellfish, he will extract the natural sweetness in the cooking process, and then concoct a suitable sauce, perhaps the narcotic alliance of brandy and cream with scallops, or something smooth and herby for a feuilleté of seafood.

With fresh fish, his sense of simplicity is perfect, and fillets of john dory, or whatever has been landed in the harbour that day, are cooked just so, retaining vigour and freshness which his use of herbs agreeably accentuates. Cahier is an assured cook, so assured, indeed, that he has no need to be verbose or gimmicky, whether he is assembling toothy moules marinière as a starter, or a super-duper tarte tatin for dessert. He simply lets the ingredients and his professional transformation of them do all the talking. Service can be a little tentative, early in the evening, but when the room fills up and everything and everybody relaxes, you find La Coquille at its best.

Open 7pm-9.30pm Mon-Sat
Closed 3 weeks in Feb (limited hours off season)
Average Price: dinner £20
Credit Cards: Visa, Access/Mastercard
10% Service Charge
Full Licence
Wheelchair Access
Children — welcome (but no special menu offered)
Vegetarians must give a day's notice
On the main street in Schull, on the left hand side as you drive into the village.

DUNWORLEY COTTAGE RESTAURANT ★
Dunworley, Butlerstown, Co Cork Tel: (023) 40314
Katherine Noren

For those who love Katherine Noren's Dunworley Cottage Restaurant, it is unimaginable to consider that there might be other folk who would not regard this sacred shrine as one of the greatest restaurants in the country. They cannot conceive of people who do not, indeed, see it as one of the most singular restaurants in the north of Europe, a wild card, a one-off.

The disciples of Dunworley point eagerly and hungrily to its protean perfection; they go quiet with awe at the purity of taste which every morsel of the food Asa Helmerson cooks exhibits so perfectly; they go wide-eyed in explanation at the elemental wildness in which the restaurant is located, and how this is so decisive and important an influence on the foods which Mrs Noren collects and cooks. If there should, ideally, be a dialogue between every restaurant and the environment from which it sources and secures its foodstuffs, then Dunworley expresses that dialogue with the finesse of a Shakesperian ode.

Dunworley hand-raised pork is peerless; the veal used in the blanquette is surely one of the greatest things you have ever eaten in your life; the smoked salmon from Frank Hedermann can have a strongwilled stomach weak with delight; the cured salmon with some salmon roe in the cream is staggering; the smoked mussels seem out-of-this-world with their etherealised allure. There is nothing to be said about the cured fish Mrs Noren prepares, and which she serves with icy glasses of aquavit, save that if you have eaten it, then you can die happy.

Some folk can't tune in to this distinctive, singular Dunworley. They find the furnishings too stark, too simple; they find the tastes too unsubdued, too urgent. The acolytes, of course, like the Shaker plainness in the design, for it doesn't distract from the food, and the acolytes say that there is nowhere else like Dunworley and that the food is unforgettable. There is only one way, of course, to discover if you are acolyte, or unimpressed, and whatever conclusion you draw, a pilgrimage to Butlerstown is mighty fun.

Open summer lunch 1pm-3pm, dinner from 6.30pm Wed-Sun
Closed Nov and Jan-early Mar
Average Price: à la carte from £6, dinner £20
Credit Cards: Visa, Access/Mastercard, Amex, Diners
No Service Charge
Restaurant Licence (plus bring your own for £2 corkage)
Wheelchair Access
Children — highchairs, half portions
Recommended for Vegetarians
The restaurant is well signposted from Timoleague, and from Clonakilty.

HEIR ISLAND RESTAURANT ➡

Island Cottage, Roaringwater Bay, Co Cork Tel: (028) 38102
John Desmond & Ellmary Fenton

If you wanted to do something unlikely, then how about this.

Open a small restaurant.

On an island.

The sort of island which means that your customers, having made their way down to the far reaches of West Cork in the first place, must, then, also make a boat journey across, in a small boat, in order to eat.

To complete this crazy idea, offer only one set menu each evening. No choice, no matter who is dining.

John Desmond and Ellmary Fenton's Island Cottage, on Heir Island off the coast of West Cork, does all these things. It represents something so magnificently unlikely and so defiantly unreal, that it was surely assured of success. Indeed, the inaccessibility of Heir Island has proven to be one of its greatest attractions.

For one thing, the boat journey across is so entrancing that you find yourself talking in Moon-in-June couplets even before you have hit the island: the sky, the sea, the instant comradeship with the other diners.

As for the food, there are important precedents for John Desmond's refusal to cook a multiple choice menu. Alice Waters in San Francisco's famed Chez Panisse offers only one dinner menu each evening. In London, Sally Clarke does the same. The only important rule about restaurant cooking, ultimately, is that it should be good, and on this Mr Desmond scores handsomely.

Skill and tactility are bedfellows in his work, and dinner is a riot of lush flavours balanced with graceful tempering, so much so that, on one memorable visit here, the entire congregation of eaters broke into spontaneous applause when Mr Desmond shyly peeked his head out of the kitchen. The food, the calm service, the camaraderie: it is not like anywhere else, or anything else, an evening on Heir Island.

Open for bookings of eight minimum (less will be accommodated if the restaurant has a booking) Mon-Sun in season (ask details of boat times)
Closed Nov-Apr
Average Price: dinner £18
No Service Charge. Boatman charges approx. £3 per head.
No Credit Cards   Wine Licence
No Wheelchair Access   Children — no facilities
No Vegetarian menu
The best boat to take leaves from Cunnamore. Driving from Skibbereen to Ballydehob, turn left at Church Cross (signposted to Heir Island). Keep going until the road ends at the Cunnamore car park.

HADDOCK

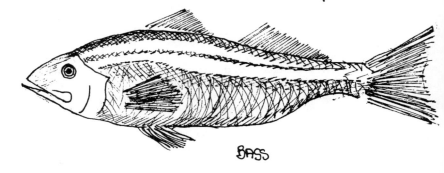

BASS

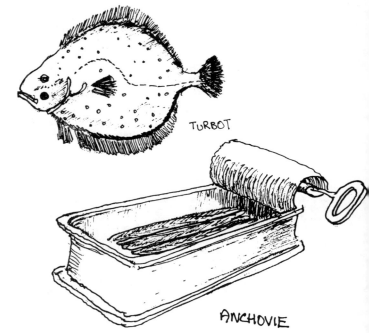

TURBOT

ANCHOVIE

ISAAC'S BRASSERIE

MacCurtain Street, Cork, Co Cork Tel: (021) 503805
Canice Sharkey

At lunchtime, with the big tall room light and bright, and the eager young staff rushing hither and thither, and the bird-call of Cork accents opening up after a slurp or two of wine, Isaac's is an altogether splendid place, a delightful space in which to enjoy Canice Sharkey's cooking.

The simplicity and informality of Mr Sharkey's food suits a simple, speedy bite — a tensely rare hamburger with a fine mushroom sauce and some demon fried potatoes; maybe some fried chicken pieces mixed with sour cream and tumbled into a pillow of pitta bread; a fine dish of tagliatelle — but the correctness and stylishness, the confidence of his cuisine, will suit a luridly long excursion, with plenty of white wine, that tails off somewhere late in the afternoon.

At dinnertime, the catholicity of Mr Sharkey's cooking always seems apt, and able to offer just what you feel like eating, whether a bowl of sweet mint and lettuce soup, good true-tasting crab cakes in the American style, a stew of beans with Clonakilty black pudding, maybe a subtle lamb curry or some of his splendid pasta. Such an international array of dishes on one menu may suggest that the food will be no more than ersatz, but Mr Sharkey is a self-controlled cook — indeed, Isaac's needs his discipline, for no one else in the kitchen can concoct this food with as much aplomb and sureness as the man himself — and the flavours in his food are as buzzy and happy as the atmosphere in the lovely dining room. The wine list is arranged by price and is excellent, service is bright and buzzy, and it is always a pleasure to be here.

Open 12.30pm-2.30pm, 6.30pm-10.30pm Mon-Sat, 6.30pm-9pm Sun
Closed Xmas
Average Price: lunch £5, dinner £7-£12
Credit Cards: Visa, Access/Mastercard
No Service Charge
Wine Licence
Wheelchair Access
Children — half price menu
Vegetarian options always available
Cork city centre, north of the river, half-way along MacCurtain Street, opposite the Metropole Hotel.

THE IVORY TOWER RESTAURANT ➡

*The Exchange Buildings, 35 Princes Street, Cork, Co Cork Tel: (021)
274665*
Seamus O'Connell

The two most important things that can be said about Seamus
O'Connell's cooking are as follows: Firstly, that he can do things other
people couldn't manage to do in a month of Sundays. Furthermore, with
the stuff they can do, he can usually do it better. Secondly, he is a chef
who is unafraid of failure: he aims for the stars, every time. When he hits
them, then you know just what a supercharged cook with a driving ambition can achieve. When he doesn't hit them, then his food is all-fall-down.
With someone else, this might be annoying. With Mr O'Connell, it is part
of his glory, the agony which attends the ecstasy of The Ivory Tower.

He is a virtuoso, with all the excitements which that description
entails. And these excitements can be intense, with menus that are
utterly thrilling just to look at, never mind to actually eat. But when you
do eat them, then, wow! A sublime gratin of asparagus and sweetbreads.
An amazing pizza of duck and aubergine, with a yeasted bread dough
base. A confit of duck served with a venison sausage and a pear and
elderflower sauce. Perfect eel boudin on red cabbage with a sorrel sauce.
This is outrageously inventive food, outrageously personal, and uncon-
cerned with commercial niceties.

"One cannot help but admire these two: their coltish beauty is
coupled with a touching, low-key sense of dignity", was how the food
writer Emily Green described Mr O'Connell and his cousin, Clare
O'Connor, with whom he shares the running of The Ivory Tower. "His
eccentricity is much more than shirt-deep", continued Ms Green. "While
he has the gentle, slightly distracted quality of a jazzman, Mr O'Connell
is a heat-and-sizzle chef, and a remarkably good one".

Like any good jazzman, Mr O'Connell also has remarkably good
taste in music, which means that not only the pots and pans rattle and
roll in The 'Tower: the sounds are ultra-cool, and so is this inspiring
space.

Open noon-4pm, 6.30pm-11pm Tue-Sun
Closed Xmas day
Average Price: lunch £5-£7, dinner £15-£20
Credit Cards: Visa, Access/Mastercard
No Service Charge
Wine Licence
No Wheelchair Access
Children — high chair
Recommended for Vegetarians
Upstairs, on the corner of Princes Street and Plunkett Street, just off Patrick's Street.
Look for the first floor sign.

LETTERCOLLUM HOUSE ➥ £

Timoleague, Co Cork Tel: (023) 46251
Con McLoughlin

"God, it's gorgeous!"

When your lunch companion utters something as effusive as this, you tend to pay attention. When they are as effusive as this, having gone no further into lunch than to break off and bite into a single piece of bread, then it is time to pay serious attention.

So, if you are having lunch or dinner in Lettercollum House, just outside the village of Timoleague, then make sure you start at the very beginning. Break off and bite into a piece of bread and, as the rush of yeasty liveliness assails your taste buds and the great span of flavour just goes on and on, try to see if you can resist such exclamations of delight. You won't get very far, believe us.

Not, at least, if the first course is a sublime seafood sausage with a note-perfect chive butter, or a mussel and pumpkin soup accented with a dash of pesto.

By the time you get to main courses, you are likely to be calling on the heavenly choirs for assistance to describe the total deliciousness of Con McLoughlin's cooking: a tarragon roast chicken so perfectly rendered that it could be the basis for a Masterclass on roasting; gorgeously creamy spanokopitta, the amazement of a plate of vegetables which have dawdled in from the walled garden and been transformed into a festival of fresh tastes.

Food this simple and pure is always a treat, no matter how often you eat it, and perfect desserts like lemon tart or floating islands with home-made vanilla ice-cream merely cap the innocent joy of eating at this funky, splendid place.

If you are five or fifty, rich or poor, frail or sound in limb and wind, Lettercollum promises delight for all. It is, probably, the most democratic dining room in the country, with all ages, creeds and complexions wrapped up by the carefree nature of the House and the "God, it's gorgeous!" food.

Open 7.30pm-9.30pm Tue-Sun, 1.30pm-3.30pm Sun (check times out of season)
Closed Xmas day
Average Price: lunch £10, dinner £13.50-£18.50
Credit Cards: Visa, Access/Mastercard, Diners
No Service Charge
Wine Licence
Wheelchair Access
Children — high chairs and half portions
Recommended for Vegetarians
Just outside Timoleague, driving west, and clearly signposted.

LISS ARD LAKE LODGE
Skibbereen, Co Cork Tel: (028) 22365
Claudia Meister

In the glorious Liss Ard Lodge, you will find some of the most singular, singularly impressive cooking in Ireland.

Claudia Meister's recipes do not use animal fats in their preparation, a bold move which forces both the chef and her assistant, Fred, into a free-fall of creativity with every single dish. What is most impressive, aside from the solid seizure of flavour which the food exhibits so boldly, is the fact that the cooking is not an abstract exercise, some sort of theme stolen from the likes of Michel Guerard. It is powerful, absorbing food, beautifully orchestrated and achieved.

Ms Meister achieves her ambition of cooking in a style which allows one to contemplate the beauty of the preparation — that startling sea-vegetable sculpting which is the leek and pine kernel cannelloni; an amazing pavé of chocolate which might have been designed by the extraordinary Japanese costume designer Eiko Ishioka, so flirty and precocious does it look on the plate — but which never masks the beauty of the flavours which the food contains. This cooking is intricate and feminine: sea scallops with a sauce vierge are evanescent; a beef consommé with foie gras parcels is as evocative an expression of unadorned beauty as is the Lodge itself.

Creativity and originality runs rampant through the six courses of dinner: a pithivier of vegetables comes in a pin-cushion pastry; little tortellinis line up like bishops' hats atop a chessboard of pulses and tapenade; a pill-box of potato accompanies a perfectly rendered roast partridge; a hot calvados soufflé is shaped like a cossack hat.

And you do not, at the end of dinner, feel that you have missed anything, or that something has been lacking. The tastes are so direct, the preparations so exquisite, the choreography of dinner so expertly conceived and executed, that you are lost in admiration. Ms Meister's food points a way forward for Irish cooking, away from the dead-hand of emulsions, the shout of butter, the cloud of cream. Anyone who wants a taste of the future — a gorgeous taste of the future — will get to Liss Ard as soon as possible.

Open 7pm-10.30pm Mon-Sun (booking essential)
Closed Xmas day
Average Price: dinner £29
Credit Cards: Visa, Access/Mastercard, Amex, Diners
No Service Charge
Full Licence
Wheelchair Access
Children — high chair
Recommended for Vegetarians
Leave Skibbereen on the Tragumna road, the house is signposted, and their tower gates — a folly — are very distinctive.

LONGUEVILLE HOUSE AND PRESIDENT'S RESTAURANT ★
Mallow, Co Cork Tel: (022) 47156 Fax: 47459
William, Jane and Aisling O'Callaghan

William O'Callaghan is an outrageously talented cook, a chef whose quiet concentration is counterpointed by a culinary imagination which seems to know no boundary. He is outrageously inventive, and marries together a virtuosic technique with a love of flavour appropriate to the countryman he is.

Added to this brilliance is a total, intense commitment to cooking: Mr O'Callaghan gets into it, he gets involved. This involvement means that, with each dish, he is on the hunt for the true, inherent flavours of the food. In the case of Longueville House, this has particular resonance. For the house is almost self-sufficient and, here, one eats the food of the house, in the house, cooked by the young chef of the house. The local food, the local house, the local boy: it is a mesmerising trio. Famous food critics have, in private moments, let it be known that they have never eaten finer food anywhere in the world, than the food they found at Longueville.

Whatever one chooses to eat is marked by pyrotechnical excellence — Longueville lamb fillets and baby courgettes set in a tomato concassé are gravity-defying; a ravioli of prawns with their juices scented with basil are secretive, hidden — and drop-dead deliciousness. William O'Callaghan's fluency extends right from the simplest fried fish — fillets of black sole with a gâteau of garden vegetables — to a crisp appreciation of fowl and game cookery — breast of farmyard duck with a ginger and coriander sauce accompanied by a potato straw cake, is something to die for. Desserts are stunningly fine: a clafoutis of garden plums with almond iced crystal; a mille feuille of wild blackberries.

Whilst eating in Longueville is a sublime indulgence, it is also a remarkably balanced one, and the courses follow seamlessly, with nothing discordant allowed to interrupt the procession of fine food.

Open to non residents Sun lunch and dinner, if pre booked
Closed late Dec-early Mar
Average Price: Sun lunch £16, dinner £26-£27
Credit Cards: Visa, Access/Mastercard, Amex, Diners
No Service Charge
Full Pub Licence
Wheelchair Access
Children — high chair
Recommended for Vegetarians
3 miles west of Mallow on the N72 to Killarney, at the big crossroads and clearly signposted.

LOVETT'S

Churchyard Lane, Well Road, Douglas, Co Cork Tel: (021) 294909 Fax:
508568
Dermod & Margaret Lovett

A certain degree of misconception surrounds Dermod Lovett's eponymous restaurant.

Because it attracts scores of businessmen, a fair proportion of whom
seem hell-bent on lengthy, boozy lunches, one might imagine it as a
dreadfully formal sort of place, keen to cater only for the credit card and
expense account set.

Furthermore, because it has one of the most select and intelligent
wine lists in the country, you might imagine it as a stuffed-shirt sort of
operation, the kind of place that might scoff if you asked for a glass of
Aussie Chardonnay.

In fact, Lovett's manages the awkward trick of successfully catering
for almost everybody, and of doing this without revealing any sense of
conflict or tension. Best of all, it is an easy and enjoyable thing to pick
and choose the type of Lovett's you wish to enjoy.

At lunchtime the food in the bar is informal, but carefully attended
to and charmingly served. If you wish for something more formal, then
the food in the restaurant is perfect for a light lunch, for the fish cookery
is always well achieved.

In the evening, the menu is more ambitious, but there is still
nothing precious about the place, and one really should endeavour to
make the most of Lovett's massive and select wine list. Mr Lovett's
concern makes this a good location to splash out on something aristo-
cratically bibulous, secure in the knowledge that the wines will have
been cosseted with care, and secure in the knowledge Mrs Lovett's food
will partner your bottle perfectly.

Open 12.30pm-2pm, 7pm-9.45pm Mon-Sat
Closed Xmas and bank holidays
Average Price: lunch £14.50, dinner £24
Credit Cards: Visa, Access/Mastercard, Amex, Diners
12.5% Service Charge
Full Pub Licence
Wheelchair Access to restaurant and bar, but not toilets
Children — welcome if well behaved
Vegetarian menu of three choices always available
From Cork take Route 609 to Douglas. Turn onto the Well Road, and the restaurant is
on your left.

MICHAEL'S BISTRO

4, Mardyke Street, Cork, Co Cork Tel: (021) 275333
Michael Clifford

A restaurant should present a challenge: a bistro must present comfort. A restaurant should supply an excitement: a bistro must supply the familiar.

It is impossible to know if Michael Clifford agonised over these theoretical matters before opening Michael's Bistro, a small room adjacent to his eponymous restaurant in Cork city. With a chef who is as famously perfectionist as this man is, it is probably a safe bet that sleepless hours were passed in ironing out details, worrying the thing to a conclusion. Happily, you need only push back the glass-inlaid doors, step onto the floorboards, and your heart breathes in all that we understand in bistro.

The food complements the concept perfectly. A bowl of cabbage soup floats on a chicken stock of perfect lightness and pointedness; cauliflower in a beer batter, with a tomato and garlic sauce, shows the fine tuning of sweet flavours, the florets crisp and fresh, the sauce was deliciously sympathetic.

With the signature dish of Irish Stew, the dish is, effectively, deconstructed, the ingredients taken apart and then re-assembled into a plate of food so earthy and generous that it seems to answer a craving in the soul rather than a simple craving of the appetite.

The pieces of lamb with their deep muttony savour are arrayed on one side, the soft cubes of potato, carrot, turnip and parsnip are on the other and ribbons of cabbage in the centre are sprinkled with pearl barley. A delicate soup of puréed vegetables lies underneath, and even with a touch of cream to finish the dish, the stew is light, full of supple flavours that are hugely satisfying.

With baby chicken, the fowl is roasted, then split, and a tumble of root vegetables acts as a stuffing, with a tarragon cream sauce underneath. Desserts are classic, and quite fab: a choux case filled with a Bailey's cream on a chocolate sauce and a fresh fruit pastry tartlet had perfect pastry, perfect custard. There is no better place in which to enjoy spuds and pearl barley, beef and cabbage, all the timeless aristocrats of the bistro.

Open noon-3pm, 6pm-10.30pm Tue-Sat
Closed Xmas Day
Average Price: meals £10-£14
Credit Cards: Visa, Access/Mastercard
No Service Charge
Wine Licence
Wheelchair Access
Children — welcome
Varied Vegetarian dishes served
A minute's walk from Jury's Hotel: turn left out the entrance, then right, and at the first set of traffic lights you will see the restaurant.

THE OYSTERCATCHER RESTAURANT ✶
Oysterhaven, Co Cork Tel: (021) 770822
Sylvia & Bill Patterson

Bill Patterson calls his starter dishes "The Seducers" — Hot Smoked Ummera Salmon on Blinis with a Leek Sauce; Oyster Sausage on a Saffron Sauce; Bresoala with Sun-dried Tomatoes and Fresh Parmesan; Grilled Inagh Goat's Cheese with Grape and Pinenut Salad; Local Oysters baked with Almonds, Garlic and Parsley.

They arrive at the table, and you begin. Voices die down, golden silence reigns. You have just been seduced.

When they are finished, responses are, usually, something like this: "The problem with this is trying to stretch it out, to make it last as long as possible", or: "I don't want to eat this, I just want to make it last".

But eat it you must. Bill Patterson's food is irresistible, as tasty as anything cooked by anyone in this country. Built on a bedrock of peerless ingredients, he works his magic, a magic that can strike one dumb.

It's not just the food in The Oystercatcher which weaves a spell, however. The restaurant itself is a picture-postcard cottage, at the cross of the road in Oysterhaven, five miles out of Kinsale and not much further from Cork city itself. Winking red lights line the eaves, and inside the room is a romantic, understated space. The glasses on the table are tall and sparkling, and one enjoys a cool sense of relaxation alongside the tingling note of expectation which a cook like Bill Patterson engenders.

Main courses merely increase the magic: Marinated Tuna Steak with Roma Tomato and Caper Sauce; King Prawns on a Garlic and Ginger Sauce with Oyster Juice; a mildly curried Breast of Chicken with a waggish poppadum on top; a Lobster Charlotte with a Basil Scented Sauce; a Tournedo topped with goat's cheese. All too soon, they are gone.

Desserts, like crème brûlée or a fresh fruit pavlova, are delicate and modest, another signature of Mr Patterson's work, for the rhythm of a dinner in The Oystercatcher starts with a bang but then works gradually towards simpler, lighter flavours. At the end, you have been seduced by beauty. And you want it to happen all over again.

Open 12.30pm-2.30pm Mon-Fri, 7pm-9.30pm Mon-Sat
Closed Xmas, Easter mid Jan-mid Feb (low season bookings absolutely essential)
Average Price: dinner £23.95
Credit Cards: Visa, Access/Mastercard, Amex
10% Service Charge on parties of six or more
Wine Licence
Wheelchair Access
Children — every effort made to accommodate them
Recommended for Vegetarians if given 24 hrs notice
Follow signs for Oysterhaven, and the restaurant is just on your left before you go over the bridge into the village.

CAFÉ PARADISO

16 Lancaster Quay, Western Road, Cork, Co Cork Tel: (021) 277939
Denis Cotter & Bridget Healy

Denis Cotter's Café Paradiso is housed in a fine big street-level room, simply and effectively decorated by the artist Eoin Kelly in voguish colours of terracotta, yellow and turquoise.

The interior is a carefree complex of tables and chairs, with a simple counter at the far end. The waitresses fetch food from the counter and, behind it, Mr Cotter, works dedicatedly.

For what Mr Cotter does, and for the way Mr Cotter cooks, this space proves apposite and appropriate. His cooking is quietly and effectively modern, and yet deceptively simple. It is annotated by a broad vision which enjoys the flavours of the Pacific Rim and the freshness of the Mediterranean. And, always, it is underpinned by a serious devotion to good flavours: this is rich food, and any sense of denial or political correctness comes a distant second to Mr Cotter's belief in successful dishes.

You shouldn't, therefore, think of Café Paradiso as a "vegetarian" restaurant. They don't cook meat, admittedly, but that is the only difference between Denis Cotter's style of cooking and that of any other good chef: the carnivore who eats here will not find that there is anything missing from the food. "We want to bring vegetarian eating into the mainstream and out of the ghetto", says Mr Cotter. Already, his cooking tastes complete of and unto itself, and Café Paradiso marks the advance of genuine creativity within vegetarian cookery in Ireland.

This gad-about nature is evident from Café Paradiso's menu: vegetable stir-fry will be fired up with a hot and sour black bean sauce, and consoled with roasted cashews and fragrant rice; fresh spinach tagliatelle with mushrooms will enjoy the punch of a soulful red wine sauce; saffron crêpes Cantona will be filled with courgettes, walnuts and cream cheese. The desserts are seriously moreish: iced spiced lemon and orange mousse with a walnut and brandy sauce; butterscotch and walnut cheesecake with cream and a warm butterscotch syrup. Voluptuous stuff. Incidentally, it can appear in here, at times, that smoking is compulsory. Don't worry. It's not.

Open 10.30am-10.30pm (lunch 12.30pm-3pm, dinner 6.30pm-10.30pm) Tue-Sat
Closed Xmas week, 2 weeks Sept and Easter
Average Price: lunch £3.60-£5.50, dinner £10-£15
Credit Cards: Visa, Access/Mastercard
No Service Charge
Wine Licence
Wheelchair Access to restaurant, but not to toilets
Children — half portions, high chairs, toys and books
Reccmmended for Vegetarians
Opposite Jury's hotel.

SHIRO JAPANESE DINNER HOUSE ➡

Ahakista, Co Cork Tel: (027) 67030
Kei and Werner Pilz

There are only two tables in the Shiro Japanese Dinner House, each in a separate room, and each available only to a single party each evening. There is only Kei Pilz and her husband, Werner, to cook and to serve, and their food is only quite extraordinary, an event which almost demands the realm of the sexual vocabulary in order to convey adequately the pleasure it gives.

In the Shiro, an ideal of heightened, almost narcotic, delight is orchestrated by Kei Pilz by means of a sinuous procession of dishes, each of them separate but, ultimately, sympathetic and harmonious. The template of this culinary alchemy is conceived as operating on a broad canvas and in a slow and steady time-flow, with that final sense of satisfaction, that pinnacle of pleasure, arising only at the conclusion of a meal.

One thinks of equivalents from other disciplines, and it seems most obvious to draw them from Japanese culture — the tension and release of a novel by Shusako Endo or maybe a movie by Yasujiro Ozua — for there can seem to be too few equivalents among the culinary arts with which to compare the experience of dinner in the Shiro.

Every delicious morsel is parcelled exquisitely, with Mrs Pilz's background as an artist finding full expression creating a procession of dishes that are a delight to the eye — the filigree fans of tempura served on a wooden board, tenderly carved vegetables, a brown Windsorish suimono with tofu and cabbage greens hidden in the soup — and a delight to the palate — smoky tea-leaved sea weed as part of Azuke-Bachi, supple sashimi of mackerel, salmon and squid. Through the course of the evening, this seems to motivate and arouse, and ultimately exhaust, every sense in the body and, finally, in its perfection, to touch upon the soul. Dinner in the Shiro Japanese Dinner House is a unique experience.

Open 7pm-9pm Mon-Sun
Closed Xmas and Jan
Average Price: dinner £33
Credit Cards: Visa, Access/Mastercard, Amex (payment by credit card incurs an additional charge of 5%)
No Service Charge
Wine Licence
No Wheelchair Access
Children — no facilities
Recommended for Vegetarians
Signposted from the Cork-Bantry road and from the village of Durrus.

TRA AMICI

Dromkeal, Coomhola Road, Ballylickey, Co Cork Tel: (027) 50235
Sean Vail

The food in Tra Amici looks, superficially at least, quite simple: Spaghetti al Pesto, Carpaccio all' Albese, Pollo alla Cacciatora, the familiar dishes we associate with Italian cuisine. Sean Vail cooks these foods the way an Italian might cook them at home in Italy and he can achieve, on occasion, an almost mysterious simplicity.

Tastes are correct and sympathetic and they are to be found throughout a meal: Vermicelli with clams, soft thimbles of gnocchi with a red sauce, delicate veal that disappears in the mouth, a fine baked cheesecake.

Mr Vail talks modestly about his cooking, describing it as "Occasion Cooking". "Italians would cook these type of dishes on special occasions: gnocchi is something the family sits down and makes for something like a wedding, or for Easter", he says.

Tra Amici, like its food, signals a general direction away from the trattoria, for it is a formal restaurant and, indeed, this formality has yet to settle down and create a relaxed space, the type of space which people expect to find when they eat Italian food. Overcoming this conundrum, and allying it with a consistent style, should see Tra Amici settle into a comfortable adolescence.

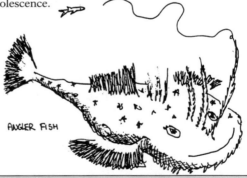

ANGLER FISH

Open 7pm-10pm Mon-Sat
Closed 1 Oct-1 Apr
Average Price: dinner £22.50
Credit Cards: Visa, Access/Mastercard
No Service Charge
Wine Licence
Wheelchair Access (incl disabled toilet)
Children — special children's menu on request
Vegetarian options always served, special requests always considered
Signposted at the Ballylickey Bridge, a few miles west of Bantry: drive up the hill from the sign.

THE VINTAGE
Kinsale, Co Cork Tel:
Raoul & Seiko de Gendre

It is good to once again have a trailblazing restaurant in Kinsale, for the self-appointed "Gourmet Capital of Ireland" has had no consistent culinary performer in the last few years. In a small town like this, it is always productive to have one restaurant which sets its standards to an international level, for where it leads, others must follow.

This year, everyone will be hanging onto the coat tails of Raoul & Seiko de Gendre's Vintage, for in the short time since this couple have taken over one of Kinsale's landmarks, they have established a reputation for cooking which can achieve very pure, almost perfect tastes: fillets of black sole sautéed belle meuniere with a lemon butter sauce scores perfectly in capturing unalloyed, simple and expressive flavours; oven roasted barbary duck will be served with a confit of its leg, offering two totally different and complementary tastes.

Best of all, there is no unnecessary fiddling about with the food: it speaks for itself. This is only right, of course, for dinner in The Vintage is expensive, and at these prices one will want to see the service settle down and a policy on smoking in the small dining room instituted. A few more wines at a decent price will mean that it would be possible to have a less expensive night out. But, despite these teething matters, this is one to watch.

Open 6.45pm-10pm Mon-Sun (closed Tues)
Closed mid Jan-mid Feb
Average Price: à la carte dinner £28
Credit Cards: Visa, Access/Mastercard, Amex
No Service Charge
Full Licence
Wheelchair Access
Children — well behaved children welcome
Vegetarian option always available
In the centre of Kinsale.

RESTAURANT ST JOHN
Fahan, Inishowen, Co Donegal Tel: (077) 60289
Reggie Ryan

Let us not disparage the virtue of certainty.

Phil McAfee's cooking in Restaurant St. John may not consist of concoctions, inventions and improvisations hauled straight from the cutting edge of the culinary world. He may not wish to dabble a toe in the waters of the Pacific Rim, he may never have read a book about blue corn and chocolate combinations — as per the Navajo Indians, or the Incas, or his great-aunt, or the late Fanny and Johnny on a bender, or whoever — but he knows what his customers like, what his customers appreciate and what they want, and he knows how to deliver it to them.

This is the secret of Reggie Ryan's enduring Restaurant St. John. It is not an ephemeral place, as are so many others in the restaurant world. Instead, it endures, year in and year out, simply by virtue of doing what they do, and making sure they do it right. They don't change just because others change, and any alterations done here will be done slowly and carefully, and revisions thought about for a long time before being put into practice.

So, expect stuffed local mussels, which will be particularly good, great staples and standards such as pork fillet with a port wine sauce or chicken breast with tarragon cream, something light and effective such as brill with lemon butter.

And you can expect careful service in the cosily suburban-styled rooms, and a splendid wine list with a selection of big guns for high rollers — Grange Hermitage, Palmer, Latour and Clos De La Roche — if you have the money to blow-out, but lots of other fine, gluggable stuff at very good prices.

Open 7pm-9.30pm Wed-Sat
Closed Xmas Day, Good Fri
Average Price: dinner £20
Credit Cards: Visa, Access/Mastercard
10% Service Charge
Restaurant Licence
Wheelchair Access
Children — no facilities
Varied Vegetarian Menu served each evening
On the left hand side of the road as you enter Fahan driving north, and clearly signposted.

CASTLE MURRAY HOUSE
Dunkineely, Co Donegal Tel: (073) 37022
Thierry Delcros

Having quietly worked his way around this place and that place in Donegal, gifting other people's restaurants and hotels with the benefit of his exquisitely attuned skills, Thierry Delcros and his wife Claire opened Castle Murray at the end of 1989. The news of their good food spread like wildfire, not just in Donegal — a county where, on all too many occasions, a meal gives you an opportunity to step back in time to about, oh, 1974, let's say — but also across the border into the North.

The reasons for this success are instantly recognisable: a happy lack of pretentiousness, inspiring food at good prices and the ability, because those prices are so keen, to stay overnight in one of their rooms and thus make a decent night of it. In the light of new legislation on drinking and driving, M. Delcros' restaurant with rooms is a fine example of how restaurants in the future will have to offer accommodation if they wish to get people to drink more than a single glass of wine.

M. Delcros' cooking style remains devotedly French, but his cooking presents a perfect marriage between disciplined techniques and glorious Irish produce: local game birds — likely shot by the man himself — fresh fish and shellfish, bio-dynamically grown vegetables, fresh eggs from run-around-the-yard chickens.

He doesn't innovate to any large extent, so you can be comforted by familiarity: there will be pâtés, rich soups, fish with sauces, meats with sauces, and you can have a dinner as simple as onion soup, then a grilled sirloin steak and some ices to finish if you wish.

But it is in the extraction of flavour and the respect for balance in a dish where we find the measure of the man. This cooking tastes right, from Tournedos façon Rossini to Braised Brill with Leeks, from McSweyne's Bay Blue Lobster to Fresh Pasta au Poisson. On a busy night service can get a little strung-out, but there is always the startlingly beautiful view, and this is food well worth waiting for.

Open 7pm-9.30pm ('till 10pm Fri and Sat) Mon-Sun, 12.30pm-2.30pm Sun
Sun Closed Xmas and Mon-Wed off season
Average Price: lunch £13, dinner £16-£22
Credit Cards: Visa, Access/Mastercard, Diners
No Service Charge
Full Licence
Wheelchair Access
Children — welcome, no special menu
Vegetarian meals with prior notice
Signposted just after the village of Dunkineely, which is west of Donegal town on the road to Killybegs.

ADRIAN'S

3 Abbey Street, Howth, Co Dublin Tel & Fax: (01) 8391696
Adrian and Catriona Holden

Adrian's is a simple little place — one room that operates for lunchtime, another that operates for dinner — and it is lively, fun, laid-back.

The restaurant should, perhaps, be more accurately called "Catriona's", for it is Adrian Holden's daughter who is the firebrand with the frying pan in her hand

Ms Holden is a young woman who looks like a teenager, cooks with the vitality of an adolescent, and the control of an expert. On one lunch-time visit to Adrian's, we asked what the chicken and tomato on garlic toast with glazed cheese was like. "Really yummy", said Ms Holden. And the mushroom and ginger soup? "Really hearty", said Ms Holden. She was right, both times: yummy and hearty. This is very moreish food: true, effective flavours

Her skills enjoy a broad template, untramelled by any conservatism: three pepper gâteau; koulibiaca with a sorrel sauce; a cornucopia of squid; rabbit casserole with little onions; parsnip and cauliflower gratin with a little salad; youthful snappy cooking, and Ms Holden manages to prime each dish so that the flavours are clambering out.

Ms Holden may appear unduly youthful, but there is a wisdom in both her culinary and her business approach which is fit for someone far beyond her years. You trust her judgement, trust her savvy, trust her desire to do her best.

You trust, above all, the fact that she understands food as a creative art, and that she herself cooks with a creative spirit. Never mind the shoestring decoration of the place, the informality: this is real cooking.

Open 12.30pm-3pm Mon-Sat, 6pm-9.30pm Mon-Sun ('till 8pm Sun)
Closed 25–26 Dec, Good Fri
Average Price: lunch £6.50-£7.90, dinner £16
Credit Cards: Visa, Access/Mastercard, Amex, Diners
No Service Charge
Wine Licence
No Wheelchair Access (but no problem to help)
Children — welcome (discuss when booking)
Vegetarians need to give advance notice
At the end of Howth village, past the pier, where the road broadens out, Adrian's is just a short stroll up the hill.

AYUMI-YA JAPANESE RESTAURANT
Newpark Centre, Newtownpark Avenue, Blackrock, Co Dublin Tel: (01) 283 1767
Yoichi Hoashi

The parent of the Ayumi-Ya Steakhouse in Dublin city, and one of the longest established restaurants in the county, the Ayumi-Ya continues to move through the years with grace and the promise of good food.

Mrs Hoashi's food is as ornamented and as fine as one expects of Japanese cooking, whether you choose the Teppan-Yaki tables and have the food cooked immediately in front of you on hot plates, or if you decide to go native, sit on the floor and enjoy the calming service by the waitresses.

The set menus are excellent value for money, but sometimes it is fun to allow the restaurant to compose a menu for you — they even suggest that first-timers choose the Omakase-Menu, where the chefs select the food — and to indulge in a succession of sublime and sinuous and sympathetic dishes: tempura with its clamouring batter wrapped around a series of fish and vegetables; tofu with its mellow indifference sharpened by deep-frying or mixed with sesame oil; shabu-shabu of thinly sliced beef washed in broth with the fire of grated radish to sharpen it up.

On an ideal evening, and casting your mind back over the years it will be hard to remember having anything other than an ideal evening, the flow of flavours will be as seamless as the sense of pleasure this food, with its perfect balance between austerity and indulgence, can engender, a sense of pleasure which everyone in the Ayumi-Ya works hard to create. Great choices for vegetarians make it extra valuable.

Open 6pm-11pm Mon-Sat, 5.30pm-9.45pm Sun
Closed Xmas, Good Fri, New Year's Day
Average Price: dinner £9.95-£14.95
Credit Cards: Visa, Access/Mastercard, Amex, Diners
No Service Charge, except for parties over 8, 10%
Restaurant Licence
Wheelchair Access to restaurant but not toilet
Children — welcome before 8.30pm, children's platter £6.95
Recommended for Vegetarians
At the Blackrock end of Newtownpark Avenue, amongst the small group of shops set back from the road by a small car park.

AT THE MERE SUGGESTION OF NOUELLE CUISINE AND OUR CHEF
JERRY McCLINTOCK LEAPS INTO ACTION. JERRY AND HIS TEAM ARE RENOWNED
WHERE EVER GOOD FOOD IS THE BY WORD.

AYUMI-YA JAPANESE STEAKHOUSE

132 Lwr Baggot Street, Dublin 2 Tel: (01) 622 0233 Fax: 662 0221
Yoichi Hoashi

You can fall in love with the food in the Ayumi-Ya, and find you crave it as much as a lover craves the company of another. These tastes are so tactile and satisfying, so intelligently realised, that they overturn our conception of Japanese food as something cool, something remote. This is friendly, lovable food.

The "steaks" are Teppan steaks, and refer to the manner in which they are cooked — over a hot iron griddle — rather than the beef, chicken, prawn, salmon or vegetable that you select, and there is a Kushi-age menu: meat, veg or seafood threaded onto skewers, breadcrumbed and deep fried.

The noodles, in great big deep bowls, need all the concentration they are given by the clientele of Japanese businessmen who scoop and slurp at the Soba — buckwheat noodles — or the Udon — wheat noodles — which bask in bowls of soup garnished with batter and deep fried tofu. Ayumi-Ya Ramen are egg noodles with caramel tasting roast pork and slivers of raw root vegetable, and there are two Japanese Pasta dishes of pan fried noodles with stir fried vegetable or cod's roe.

If you cannot make it to eat in the Ayumi-Ya, take heart, and take a Bento to go. "The Bento began when people would go to the sumo, the theatre, the kabuki", says Mrs Akiko Hoashi, "It's portable food".

The common feature of any Bento is rice — either boiled or fried — but from that point on you can change any of the accompaniments: Makunouchi Bento, in a large, rectangular box, may comprise boiled rice with a little pickle on top, then some breaded and fried Prawn Ebifrai, a little macaroni salad in dressing, some chicken Toritasuta-Age, a portion of superb salted and grilled mackerel, a smattering of grilled leeks and peppers and deliciously sweet butterbeans. Yakitori Bento offers skewered, grilled pieces of chicken and onion, full of succulent, baleful tastes, and the cleansing macaroni, sweet butterbeans and toothsome rice.

Open 12.30pm-2.30pm, 6pm-11.30pm Mon-Sat
Closed Xmas, New Year and Good Friday
Average Price: lunch from £6.50, dinner £10.95-£13.95
Credit Cards: Visa, Access/Mastercard, Amex
10% Service Charge after 6pm　　Wine Licence
No Wheelchair Access (though they are happy to carry wheel-chair bound customers down the stairs)
Children — welcome until 8.30pm, high chair, children's platter £6.95
Recommended for Vegetarians
On the corner of Lwr Baggot Street and Lwr Pembroke Street, 5 mins walk from St Stephen's Green.

CAPERS

4 Nassau St, Dublin 2 Tel: (01) 679 7140
Eddie Bates

There will be many who will rejoice long and loud at the news that Eddie Bates has returned to his old stomping ground, upstairs over the vegetable shop in Nassau Street.

When Mr Bates cooked here some years back, he established a reputation for food which exhibited a modest flair and a knock-'em-dead understanding of flavour. Boldly amateurish and unconstrained by any formality, Capers produced soulful, delicious food at the right price in the right place, with cool sounds and an enjoyably threadbare decor.

Well, for those who have missed it, here it is again: those excellent mussels steamed with cider, apples and scallions, as toothy, rich and bright with flavour as ever; excellent roasted peppers stuffed with feta cheese, black olives and basil, then topped with a herb crust; chicken breast is pan-fried and served with fine cous-cous and a hot aubergine and pepper sauce; rack of lamb is cooked just right, with a fitting partner in a provençal sauce.

Mr Bates' cooking has always been a model of effective simplicity, and in Capers he has the perfect space for his unpretentious, enjoyable cooking.

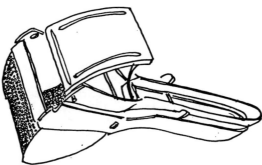

Open noon-3pm Mon-Fri, 6.30pm-late Thur-Sat
Closed Xmas and bank holidays
Average Price: lunch £5-£6, dinner £12-£15
No Credit Cards
No Service Charge, except for parties of over 5, 10%
Wine Licence
No Wheelchair Access
Children — welcome
Recommended for Vegetarians
Next to the Kilkenny Design Centre, and above the Runner Bean vegetable shop.

CHINA-SICHUAN RESTAURANT
4 Lower Kilmacud Road, Stillorgan, Co Dublin Tel: (01) 288 4817 Fax: 288 0882
David Hui

Banish from your mind the vague memory of those beloved sizzling dishes which you scoff, somewhat tipsy, on tipsy Saturday nights in your local Chinese eating house, those fake concoctions of MSG and culinary myopia.

Here, in David Hui's China-Sichuan, up in dreary, dull old Stillorgan, you will find the counterpoint to that hideously compromised cooking which we believe is Chinese food. In the China-Sichuan you find the real thing: Hot & Sour Soup with a musky, coffee-odoured thrill of a taste; pan fried dumplings with a fathom-black dipping sauce or in a hot sauce with spicy chilli; chicken in a garlic sauce, the dish offering endless nodes of viscous flavours; some monkfish with cashews perhaps, the fish jumping with freshness and the tentacular cuts putting you in mind of the roof of the Sydney Opera House.

With these, some voluptuously slinky Dan-Dan Mein noodles, or maybe some clean boiled rice. Mr Li, the cook, rarely puts a cleaver wrong, and the excitement of tastes which a dinner can deliver is one of the city's delights. Expect to cough, occasionally, as the toxic charge of chillies hits the back of the throat: apply cool white wine immediately. For dessert, then, some gloriously cool almond bean curd, the taste like an incredibly exotic marzipan, comes as a delicious surprise, the perfect ending to a series of surprisingly accessible and yet delightfully authentic tastes. Service is excellent, design is strictly unreconstructed over-the-top, and this is an invaluable Chinese restaurant.

Open 12.30pm-2.30pm, 6pm-11pm Mon-Sun (lunch from 1pm Sun)
Closed Xmas
Average Price: lunch £8, dinner £16.50
Credit Cards: Visa, Access/Mastercard, Amex
10% Service Charge
Wine Licence
Wheelchair Access to restaurant but not to toilet
Children — high chair
Recommended for Vegetarians
The restaurant is 100 yds from the Stillorgan Shopping Centre, on the Kilmacud Road, in the midst of a group of shops.

THE COMMONS RESTAURANT
St. Stephen's Green, Dublin 2 Tel: (01) 475 2597
Michael Fitzgerald

Serenity is the keynote of The Commons. Nothing, but nothing, disturbs the steady flow of the way in which they do business in here.

Nothing disrupts the calm of the staff. A pacific, almost zen-like abstractedness, surrounds the styling, the service, the raison d'être.

You can criticise this, and wish that the restaurant was funkier — a recent reviewer wrote that "One found oneself longing for a nice rowdy table who drank more than they meant to, constantly interrupted each other and laughed too loud at each others' jokes" — and you might wish that the food was punchier in taste, not just so totally tasteful.

But to do so is to miss the point. It is in not being rowdy that The Commons works. It is not the sort of place which begins the beginning of a long, long night that ends up in some basement club with a bottle of warm Muscadet in front of you at 5 a.m. Its formality is its greatest strength. Its sublimation of any overt character, any particular sense of place or "Irishness", is something it strives to achieve, and something it does achieve.

It is poised, and precise. It is where you go when entertaining — clients from out of town, that aunt you haven't seen for years and who you hope will bequeath you some money, a success in some exam or some promotion. And, because they know that you have business of some nature or other on your mind, the staff never intrude, and they make sure that nothing intrudes.

Michael Bolster's food is just one more facet of this serenity. Though it reads modern and involved on the menu — warm oysters with mango and leeks with a white wine sabayon; halibut with haricot vert; roast monkfish in bacon with colcannon; a pithivier of vegetables with sauerkraut; foie gras and grilled black pudding with a pear purée — but this is not food to slap you about the head. Instead, its luxuriousness and correctness seduces quietly. Like everything else.

Open 12.30pm-2.30pm, 6pm-11pm Mon-Sun (lunch from 1pm Sun)
Closed Xmas
Average Price: lunch £18, dinner £29.50
Credit Cards: Visa, Access/Mastercard, Amex, Diners
15% Service Charge
Full Licence
Wheelchair Access (through back door)
Children — no facilities
Vegetarian dishes always available
In the basement of Newman House, beside the St Stephen's Green Church on St Stephen's Green South.

COOKE'S CAFÉ

14 South William Street, Dublin 2 Tel: (01) 679 0536/7/8
John Cooke

The changes visited on John Cooke's eponymous café over the last year have been not just physical alterations — the restaurant has expanded both upstairs and down, with a new entrance and more spacious seating — but also intellectual changes, which have seen the promise of this fine space blossom into real, creative, food.

Where, previously, the menus disported themselves amidst the complexities of Cal-Ital cooking and brought forth a range of dishes that were usually well-achieved but which seemed to present endless problems of service — it is extremely difficult to cook and sauce and serve pasta correctly, unless you are born in Bologna or are a spiritual heir of Marcella Hazan — the newer menus are much more compact and intelligent, and the troublesome pasta dishes are confined to a scattering of choices: fettucine al vodka, or angel hair with grilled aubergines, tomato, basil and olive oil as starters; angel hair vongole or tortelloni au gratin as main courses.

This has allowed more room for the strengths of the kitchen: excellent fish and shellfish cookery — seabass en papillotte with a ragout of mussels, clams, saffron, tomato, herbs and olive oil is an knock-out compendium dish, and the staff almost know how to open the parcel properly, whilst something as simple as fried calamari is perfectly executed — and soulful experiments with offal and game: fine roast partridge with a celeriac purée; mallard with braised red cabbage and a Madeira butter sauce; perfect duck liver with a concasse of tomato; veal liver and veal kidney both expertly rendered.

One gets the sense, also, that the kitchen is happier with this simpler, home-based style of food, so that air of frantic mishap which used to permeate the café is gone. Some things have not changed, however. Whilst the staff are slightly more relaxed than previously, they are still adolescently self-conscious. On a happier note, John Cooke's signature is still a byword for stylish, groovy food. There are many other cooks in Dublin who are attempting something similar to Cooke's Café, but the original remains the best.

Open 12.30pm-6pm lunch, 6pm-11.30pm dinner Mon-Sun
Closed Xmas and bank holiday lunches
Average Price: lunch £13.50, dinner £13.50-£25
Credit Cards: Visa, Access/Mastercard, Amex, Diners
10% Service Charge
Wine Licence
Wheelchair Access (with advance notice only)
Children — welcome
Vegetarian options always available
At the back of the Powerscourt Townhouse Centre, on the corner at the zebra crossing.

LE COQ HARDI

35 Pembroke Road, Dublin 4 Tel: (01) 668 4130/668 9070
John and Catherine Howard

The public perception of John Howard's restaurant, throughout its long history, has always been of an archetypal bourgeois eating palace, somewhere that slings culinary history right back to the days of César Ritz and Auguste Escoffier, a restaurant which offers an uninterrupted blow-out of classic cuisine and claret.

Yet, whilst this image can be true, and whilst the restaurant does like to present itself as someplace where racehorse owners can land their helicopters after a successful day at the Curragh before they begin to fritter away their winnings on Haut-Brion and hâute cuisine — a tureen of Dublin Bay Prawns scented with cognac, a millefeuille of Irish salmon with a watercress butter sauce, a fricassée of monkfish with black noodles, coq au vin in a pastry dome — there is actually as much of the soft and ageless nature of French peasant cuisine to be found here as there is cooking that is grandiose and verbose.

You can enjoy long-cooked oxtail braises, plump terrines of rabbit, chicken liver and leek, hake with tomato, olives, olive oil and mashed potato, Mr Howard's own invention of potato cakes with Clonakilty black pudding and fried apples. There will be perfectly cooked root vegetables, and the prices for the set meals are very fair.

If you do have a successful day at the Curragh, of course, then the carte in the Coq will soak up plenty of that easy-come money, and then there is one of the best and priciest wine lists in the entire country, just waiting to account for the rest.

Open 12.30pm-3pm Mon-Fri, 7pm-11pm Mon-Sat
Closed Xmas and 2 weeks in early Aug
Average Price: lunch £18, dinner £28-£45
Credit Cards: Visa, Access/Mastercard, Amex, Diners
12.5% Service Charge
Full Restaurant Licence
No Wheelchair Access
Children — no facilities
Varied Vegetarian dishes served each evening, notice helps
On the right hand side, when driving from Baggot Street towards the junction at Ballsbridge.

HILE HE WAS IN THE ARMY
M WON TWO MEDALS BOXING
R HIS TEAM (LIGHT-HEAVY) —
PRESENTING SOUTHERN COMMAND.
M ALSO WON A BRONZE AT
YMPIA FOR AN ICE CARVING
S FAIRY WAS HIGHLY
OMMENDED.

L'ECRIVAIN

109 Lwr Baggot Street, Dublin 2 Tel: (01) 661 1919, Fax: 661 0617
Derry & Sally-Anne Clarke

Derry Clarke's move upstairs from his old basement restaurant to a new street-level premises just a step-off Baggot Street, will see some changes in his method of working.

There will be a cheaper two-course lunch, and experiments every-whichway as the new kitchen is knocked into shape, and as Mr Clarke's team grapple with the ability to seat 60 covers, more than double the number they could handle in the old basement.

But what will not change is this: Mr Clarke cooks soulful food with a generous heart, and his team are just about the best in the business. They are so good, indeed, that they could give masterclasses in the art of serving food and wine. They are the sort of people who, when you give them your coat, make you feel as if you have also divested yourself of all worldly responsibility, just by walking in the door. Well, for a couple of hours anyway.

Mr Clarke, meantime, could give masterclasses in the business of creating a cuisine which manages to be both very classical and yet very personal. This is his food, his style. He continues to work in a tradition which, for many cooks, has come to represent something of a culinary cul-de-sac: Cuisine Française is often misrepresented in this country, because cooks overcomplicate the processes needed to prepare the food.

Where Mr Clarke resurrects this style is in preparing the dishes with spontaneity and originality. He is a very commonsensical cook and a man who never loses sight of the fact that his job is to get food out to the customer in a pristine, perfect state, full of taste, full of flavour.

As a disciple of Cuisine Française, he is at his best with the sharp, succulent flavours of meat and shellfish: char-grilled scallops; a fine lobster consommé; rack of lamb scented with garlic and rosemary, and mouthwateringly carved at the table; mignons of beef with tarragon; grilled oysters. Classic, ageless food, classic tastes.

Open 12.30pm-2pm Mon-Fri, 6.30pm-11pm Mon-Sat
Closed Xmas and bank holidays
Average Price: lunch £10, dinner £23.95
Credit Cards: Visa, Access/Mastercard, Amex, Diners
10% Service Charge on food only
Full Licence
No Wheelchair Access
Children — no facilities
Full Vegetarian menu
Across the road from the Bank of Ireland, through the Archway.

ELEPHANT & CASTLE
18 Temple Bar, Dublin 2 Tel: (01) 679 3121
Liz Mee & John Hayes

Ever since it opened, in the late 1980s, many people seem to have imagined that the success of the Elephant & Castle from the day it opened its doors was, and is, based on some simple formula, something you merely have to crack into and, voila!, you too will be in charge of a restaurant which is packed to the rafters morning, noon and night.

The truth of the matter, of course, is that no one has succeeded in replicating the success of this potent palace of food.

The failure of the copy-cats has lain, usually, in their refusal to believe that there is, in fact, no formula behind this simple, bare-floorboards 'n' t-shirts place. If there is no formula, however, then perhaps there is a secret, and we might borrow an album title from R.E.M., those aristocrats of rock'n'roll, and say that the secret of the E&C, the secret of its Monster success, is that it is Automatic For The People.

Night and day, it serves the food you want, and becomes the place you want it to be. From 8-in-the-morning omelette breakfasts, to a mid-morning gouter, to a pasta lunch with a girlfriend, maybe a late afternoon pick-me-up tuna and guacamole sandwich, or pre-theatre chicken wings that have you licking your fingers right through the performance, then onwards to a late night romantic rendezvous with a loved-one, even post-pub burger and fried potatoes, perhaps a family table for Sunday brunch.

All of the foods for all of these occasions can be found here.

The food is democratically priced, but never cheap: with these ingredients it could never be. The basic menu has evolved little, and any innovation and experimentation comes from the daily specials: lamb korma with relishes; fettucini with chicken, shiitake mushrooms and asparagus, grilled fillet steak and rouille served with herb mashed potato; Sichuan chicken with spicy stir-fried noodles. Whatever you eat, it will be part of an ideal of service and simplicity which announces itself as Automatic For The People.

Open 8am-11.30pm Mon-Fri, 10.30am-midnight Sat, noon-11.30pm Sun
Closed Xmas
Average Price: lunch £3-£7, dinner £15
Credit Cards: Visa, Access/Mastercard, Amex, Diners
No Service Charge (except 10% for groups of 8 or more)
Wine Licence
Wheelchair Access
Children — welcome
Vegetarian options always available
In Dublin's Temple Bar, just on the south side of the River Liffey.

LES FRERES JACQUES
74 Dame Street, Dublin 2 Tel: (01) 679 4555
Jean-Jacques and Suzy Caillebet

There are plenty of people, judicious people, thoughtful people — even judicial people — who will select Les Freres Jacques as their favourite Dublin restaurant.

It is easy to see why. Walk down the little lane and through the door and the restaurant invites you in with that dim-lit light that suggests Parisian oyster bars or London clubs, suggests privacy and cosseting and pleasure. It's a cliché, and one hell of a nice one.

And the food in Suzy and Jean-Jacques Caillebet's restaurant is, whilst clichéd, almost always effective, almost always food that congratulates your choice of restaurant. Francophiles will delight in mussel and fennel soup; some lobster ravioli with a fillet of turbot; grilled oysters; lobster from the tank; confit de canard, crème brûlée or vanilla bavarois. The food is classic, and they do it right.

Because they do it right, the fact that a bill can quickly add up hardly seems to matter, though one should be careful when straying away from the set menus, for this can send the addition into the stratosphere, even without the steep service charge. Disappointingly, the waiting staff behave as if a tip is their God-given right.

For special occasions, and especially for business lunching, the restaurant has that assured rhythm which derives from experience and confidence, but they don't let it slip into swagger, and their Gallic correctness has, over the years, been tempered with an Irish affability. It is a very French restaurant, but it is very definitely in Dublin.

Open 12.30pm-2.30pm Mon-Fri, 7.30pm-10.30pm Mon-Sat (Fri & Sat 'till 11pm)
Closed Xmas and bank holidays
Average Price: lunch £13, dinner £20
Credit Cards: Visa, Access/Mastercard, Amex
12.5% Service Charge
Full Licence
No Wheelchair Access
Children — no facilities
Not suitable for Vegetarians
A few doors down from the Olympia Theatre on Dame Street, just across from Dublin Castle.

FURAMA CHINESE RESTAURANT
88 Donnybrook Road, Dublin 4 Tel: (01) 283 0522
Rodney Mak

One of the most pleasing aspects of the Furama is not just that their Chinese food is better than most other Chinese cooking in Dublin, or that the design of the restaurant is less garish and more commodiously bourgeois than other Chinese restaurants in Dublin. No, what cheers especially is the fact that their efforts to maintain authenticity, and to cook true Chinese food, are met by such an appreciative audience.

At weekends, the Furama is full of Dublin 4 types — weekend-access fathers spoiling their kids, rugby souls already tanked up on a few bevvies of beer, skinny women discussing their career curves — all of them enjoying the lush accents and sensual flavours which Freddie Lee's food delivers to the diner. If you have only ever sampled that dull compromise which is Chinese take-away food, then you are in for a treat: this is serious cooking.

King Prawn in spicy minced pork; roasted duck with its oily, smoky allure; black sole drunken style; green peppers stuffed with prawns in a garlic and black bean sauce; excellent seafood which includes scallops in black bean sauce, steamed sea bass and excellent lobster. If you are expert in these matters and choose cleverly, or are inexpert and ask advice, then a meal in The Furama will comprise a thrilling series of flavours and textures, a panorama of delight.

Indeed, The Furama exploits more varied techniques than most Chinese restaurants — and extends this to silver service at table when it comes to filleting fish — so there is much greater variety to be enjoyed than you will find elsewhere. The price you pay for this care is, appropriately, somewhat higher than other restaurants, and it is worth every penny.

Open 12.30pm-2pm Mon-Fri, 6pm-11.30pm Mon-Sat, 1.30pm-11pm Sun
Closed Xmas
Average Price: lunch £6.50-£12, dinner £17.50
Credit Cards: Visa, Access/Mastercard, Amex, Diners
10% Service Charge
Restaurant Licence
Wheelchair Access (but not to toilet)
Children — welcome, but no facilities
Vegetarians please ask advice and they will happily amend the menu
Opposite Bective rugby ground, as you drive out of Donnybrook going south. Near the Shell Garage.

RESTAURANT PATRICK GUILBAUD ➥
46 James Place, Baggot Street Lwr, Dublin 2 Tel: (01) 676 4192
Patrick Guilbaud

Patrick Guilbaud's eponymous restaurant is claustral in its pursuit of a classic idea of French food, as pernickity as Martin Luther when it comes to the edicts of cooking. "We are very classical", M. Guilbaud will tell you. "All our sauces are the way they should be done. If we say we do a beurre blanc we do a beurre blanc, if we do a bearnaise we do a bearnaise, but the real way. We do everything the way it should be done".

And this is true, and can make, on occasion, for exceptional eating in an elegant space, and you will find you can recall, years later, the procession of tastes in lunch or dinner: turbot with a Seville orange and ginger sauce; roast monkfish basted with honey and balsamic vinegar; veal sweetbreads with lemon and coriander. The precision of tastes which chef Guillaume Lebrun can disclose from ingredients is never less than impressive, though seasoning is always slightly on the aggressive side.

And yet, despite the protestations of affection and delight from many who have eaten here over the past dozen years, for many more Guilbaud's is a restaurant that is easy to admire, yet difficult to love. You admire the hard-headed determination, the well-drilled staff with their cloche synchronicity honed to the nth degree, the keenness of the prices for set menus, and what Molly O'Neill of the New York Times called "the refined restraint of his cuisine".

But admiring is one thing, and affection another, and Guilbaud's has never dispensed with its air of cool distance, of knowingness. This makes it perfect for entertaining, of course, for they get on with their work while you get on with yours and they never, but never, get in the way. But, if you cherish humour, spontaneity, and cooking that comes from the heart rather than the head, then other cooks, and other restaurants, may be more beguiling. Perhaps a dozen years ago it was okay to behave as if you were giving folk a Masterclass in dining. These days it just seems passé.

Open 12.30pm-2pm, 7.30pm-10.15pm Tues-Sat
Closed Xmas and bank holidays
Average Price: lunch £18.50, dinner £30
Credit Cards: Visa, Access/Mastercard, Amex, Diners
15% Service Charge
Full Licence
Wheelchair Access
Children — high chair
Vegetarian meal with prior notice
In a lane behind the Bank of Ireland, on Baggot Street.

KAPRIOL RESTAURANT

45 Camden Street Lwr, Dublin 2 Tel: (01) 475 1235 (298 5496 home)
Egidia and Giuseppe Peruzzi

It tends to be Italian restaurants which are the ones we most want to be friendly, unfussy, enduring little Mom'n'Pop sort of places.

Places where they know your name, where you go late on a Friday night, or perhaps early on a Tuesday in order to salve some domestic bruising. A place which you select as your first choice to celebrate a good punt at the races, an exam scraped through, a job secured. Egidia and Giuseppe Peruzzi's Kapriol is that place.

Most of the customers are so well known to the Peruzzis that they almost order their food in pidgin Italian. That is, if they do bother to order food, and don't just let Egidia see what she can come up with which will take their fancy. The fire will be burning away in the grate, the seats are like little cubicles wrapped around with wood, and the interior design was in fashion sometime in the middle of the century, though that may not necessarily have been this century. It is ageless.

Egidia cooks the way she has always cooked: risotto alla veneziana; fettucine doppio burro; scallopine alla marsala o limone; chicken involtini; a timeless series of tunes and symphonies of flavour. It ain't broke, so they don't try to fix it.

Giuseppe, meanwhile, looks after the wines and the front of house, and to surrender to his judgement when it comes to something to drink is wisdom itself. There are rarities on this list which you will not find elsewhere, and Mr Peruzzi is a wise wine man.

The Kapriol is not to everyone's taste — often, one suspects, this lies with the fact that this is an expensive place, where many people believe that Italian food should always be cheap — but, here, you are paying for individuality, for individual attention and for individual cooking. These are the true characteristics of a Mom'n'Pop place, someplace in which to heal, someplace in which to celebrate.

Open 7.30pm-midnight (last orders) Mon-Sat
Closed bank holidays and 3 weeks in Aug
Average Price: dinner £20-£25
Credit Cards: Visa, Access/Mastercard, Amex, Diners, JCB
12.5% Service Charge
Wine Licence
Wheelchair Access (but not to toilets)
Children — welcome
Varied Vegetarian dishes served each evening
At the southern end of Camden Street, on the corner where the road divides, on the left hand side, opposite the Bleeding Horse pub.

LA STAMPA

35 Dawson Street, Dublin 2 Tel: (01) 677 8611/677 3336
Paul Flynn

Paul Flynn is such a fine cook that one wishes he had a benefactor who would grant him a small restaurant, a large kitchen brigade, and a beautiful room in which to serve his creations.

Well, he has the last of this trilogy of dreams — La Stampa, a converted guildhall, is the most glorious restaurant room in the city, in fact in the country.

But, in the real world of commerce in which restaurants must work, Mr Flynn cooks in a restaurant which turns over very large numbers of covers. And he manages it with a small brigade.

And Mr Flynn is such a good cook that, despite the pressures of this system, he still creates good food. We must ascribe this, perhaps, to the discipline learnt at the right hand of the tempestuous Nico Ladenis, with whom Mr Flynn worked in his various London restaurants for almost a decade. The discipline of fine fish cookery which he learnt there still stands to him: baked sea bream with a dash of sesame oil is one of those successes whose merit rests entirely on simplicity and timing, and confidence.

It is the sort of dish, also, with which Mr Flynn seems most at home. He appears to have abandoned the early, modish revisions of certain Irish staples like colcannon, or bacon and cabbage, which used to feature, and he is most at home with classic bistro fare such as confit of duck, or — again a dish which needs simplicity, timing and confidence — pan fried calf's liver, or the calf's liver grilled with pancetta. These are his dishes, and they are the dishes to go for: he is a purist, not an innovator, and most at home with brasserie standbys such as boudin of chicken, or millefeuille of lamb, or a blanquette of veal.

As you might expect in a beautiful room, the beautiful people are one of the staples of La Stampa, which makes the restaurant slightly self-conscious. The staff are also slightly self-conscious, except for the restaurant manager, Declan Maxwell. Mr Maxwell is a genius at people-handling, and it is purest joy just to watch him at work.

Open 12.30pm-2.30pm Mon-Fri, 6.30pm-11.15pm Mon-Sun ('till 11.45pm Fri & Sat)
Closed Xmas
Average Price: lunch £12.50, dinner £24-£36
Credit Cards: Visa, Access/Mastercard, Amex, Diners
No Service Charge (except 10% for parties of 6 and over)
Restaurant Licence
No Wheelchair Access
Children — no facilities
Vegetarian options always available
Opposite the Mansion House at the St. Stephen's Green end of Dawson Street.

LOCKS

1 Windsor Terrace, Portobello, Dublin 8 Tel: (01) 4543391
Claire Douglas

You notice Locks, Claire Douglas' restaurant, from a distance, struck initially by the impressive mien of this handsome corner building. It looks perfect, meticulous, well-groomed, indeed.

Inside, it is just as you would have hoped, and perhaps expected: elegantly lit, fastidiously organised, a truly pleasing space. You could suggest that it is a little old-fashioned in style, but it isn't: it is timeless, because it is classic. There is something of the elegance of a brasserie about the shape of the room, and yet something club-like about the atmosphere. It is a seductive place, one of those restaurants where you slide and sink into its ambience, reluctantly emerging a few hours later, disappointedly slinking back into the real world.

Ms Douglas' theory about restaurants is one of the soundest and most sensible you could hope to hear: "The food has got to be very, very good, but there is no point in serving good food if there is no atmosphere. If I have the choice I will always go to a restaurant where I know the food is good, but I also know the ambience is good. It's a matter of finding the balance between the two", she says.

Succinctly, and completely, this summarises the ethos of Locks. Good atmosphere. Attention to vital details such as spangly, sparkly glasses, good linen, bright fires, helpful service. It's a form of magic, and a form of magic which the cooking accentuates: deep-fried goujons of sole with perfect tartare sauce; fine soups such as cream of broccoli; a clever twist with salmon en croute which is a hollandaise studded with caraway seeds; the sharp rejoinder of a gin and juniper sauce with magret of duck; an astonishingly good creme brulée. Classic cooking, done right, with a fine wine list to complement it.

People love coming here, love being here. The audience of professional folk who are devotees of its solid and classical French-style food tend to behave like little puppies getting their tummies tickled. But then, it is nice to get one's tummy tickled, on occasion.

Open 12.30pm-2pm Mon-Fri, 7.15pm-11pm Mon-Sat
Closed Xmas week and bank holidays
Average Price: lunch £13.95, dinner £22
Credit Cards: Visa, Access/Mastercard, Amex, Diners
12.5% Service Charge
Full Licence
Wheelchair Access
Children — welcome
Vegetarian dishes available (please give notice)
Between Portobello Bridge and Harold's Cross Bridge, facing the Grand Canal.

101 TALBOT
101–102 Talbot Street, Dublin 2 Tel: (01) 8745011
Margaret Duffy and Pascal Bradley

Margaret Duffy and Pascal Bradley's 101 Talbot has quietly manoeuvred itself into a position where it is not just one of the best restaurants in the capital, and not just one of the most admired, but easily one of the most enjoyed, and enjoyable.

Everything this astute and amusing pair do is devoted to making 101 a special space in which to enjoy good food, good wine, good times. Walk up the stairs, away from the interesting grot of Talbot Street, and this cocoon of calm space, cool sounds, funky grub and sweet service sets your soul at ease.

You can cast your mind back over many meals eaten here during the last few years — lunches with mile-a-minute gossip amongst your mates, quiet solo mid-afternoons with just some pasta and the news-paper to peruse, happy dinners where bottle after bottle of Fetzer Fumé Blanc or Wolfie Blass's Cab Sauv are resolutely demolished in the cause of good cheer — and what is consistent is just how much the charm, the youthfulness and the bonhomie of 101 has contributed to the cause of enjoying lunch or dinner.

Margaret Duffy's food always tastes like something which she has, firstly, enjoyed cooking and, secondly, something which she would like to eat herself. The food is so enjoyably friendly, so consumable!, for heaven's sake, that you will likely find yourself day-dreaming about that parsnip soup or that perfectly baked fillet of cod, find yourself fondly recalling that brioche of vegetables with a blue cheese dressing, or that clever dish where chicken is stuffed with olives, sun-dried tomatoes and mozzarella, that pecan pie or those oranges in caramel and Cointreau.

The personality of 101 is exuded through the food and the great service, and this bubbly, warm personality is what makes 101 so special. Without Margaret and Pascal it would be just another space. Thanks to them, and their lack of pretention, their wisdom, it is invaluable.

Open 10am-3pm Mon, 10am-11pm Tue-Sat (lunch served noon-3pm, dinner served 6pm-11pm)
Closed Xmas and bank holidays
Average Price: lunch £5-£10, dinner £12-£15
Credit Cards: Visa, Access/Mastercard, Amex, Diners
No Service Charge, except for parties of over 8 persons, 10%
Full Bar Licence
No Wheelchair Access   Children — high chairs
Recommended for Vegetarians
Talbot Street runs parallel to Abbey Street, and 101 is minutes from the Abbey Theatre.

THE RAJDOOT

26–28 Clarendon Street, Westbury Centre, Dublin 2 Tel: (01) 679 4274
Amarjit Gill

The Rajdoot offers not just the best Indian cooking in the city of Dublin, but the finest and most alluring Indian cooking in the country. Whilst it is one part of a small smart chain of Indian restaurants based in the U.K., the Dublin outpost has distinguished itself by an impressive consistency over the years, a consistency that has made it a consistently interesting and enjoyable place to eat.

Part of a chain it may be, but the calm, darkly-lit placidity of the entrance area, with its leather camel stools and soak-me-up sofas, its embroidered brass bowls filled with torchy-spicy nuts, chase away any feeling of factory-line production. The Rajdoot has its own character: efficient, aristocratic, gentle.

The food echoes this character in its stylish, instinctive, reverberant Moghul meld of almonds, yogurt, spices and butter. But the food does not trade solely on the great standards of this glorious cuisine: whilst Chicken Tikka is an institution of Northern Indian food, Tandoori Mackerel or Tandoori Quail are more unusual.

Yet, with both, the restaurant succeeds in feathering the suprisingly subtle tastes of a spicy marinade with the charcoal smoke from the tandoor oven. This finesse and delicacy — attributes which, sadly, one rarely associates with the style of cooking from the sub-Continent which one finds in Ireland — is evident in every dish in the Rajdoot: the biryanis suffuse rice with the perfume of cloves, the small selection of curries — makhani, jalferezi, bhuna and pasanda — are marvellously precise in flavour and texture, whilst the fried sundries — the bhajees, the parathas — are crisply reviving in their salty oiliness.

Breads are more than marvellous, forming an integral part of the meal should you abandon utensils and choose to use your fingers. Happily, vegetarians are almost spoilt for choice. The service is formal and the prices keen, and this is memorable food.

Open noon-2.30pm, 6.30pm-11.30pm Mon-Sat
Closed Xmas, New Year's Day, Good Fri (limited opening bank holidays)
Average Price: lunch £6.95, dinner £17.50-£19.50
Credit Cards: Visa, Access/Mastercard, Amex, Diners
12.5% Service Charge
Full Licence
Wheelchair Access (happy to help negotiate steps, but no access to toilets)
Children — welcome
Recommended for Vegetarians, 4-course dinner £14.50
At the back of the Westbury Hotel, between Wicklow St and Chatham St.

RED BANK RESTAURANT

*7 Church Street, Skerries, Co Dublin Tel: (01) 849 1005 Fax: (01) 849
1598*
Terry McCoy

The way Terry McCoy does it, being chef and patron of a restaurant
seems a piece of cake.

First, source your foods from local growers, local suppliers, local
fishmongers and fish smokers.

Get your oysters from Carlingford Lough, conveniently just up the
road. Get your flour from local flour grinders, in this case The White
River Mill, in Dunleer, conveniently just up the road. You do this in
order that the foods of the region will have the tastes of the region.

What you do, then, is to complete the equation, and cook them in
the region, exploiting your own techniques, and gently introduce the
occasional innovation that has come from a trip abroad, where you
learnt of some alliance or some suitable technique, which you find can
be made to work in your own kitchen.

Cook, then, with grace and good humour, and get things right:
steamed cockles and oysters; hake with the energetic kick of horseradish;
warm smoked salmon with a tarragon cream; crab meat mixed with sherry
and cream before baking; haddock — and here we see the influence of
travel — with Creole spices; wings of skate with spring onions, perhaps a
smoked loin of pork, or roasted Barbary duck.

The meat dishes in The Red Bank, like everything else, will be correct and flavorful, but it is with fish and shellfish that Mr McCoy
shines, and you find yourself going "ooh" and "aah" with pleasure at
the succulence and promise of each mouthful.

McCoy's object, as he himself will say, is to treat the foods with
"sympathy and respect". But he also knows that fish cookery is all about
sources — local sources — and sauces. And he knows this better than just
about anyone. Expect to have a great time.

Open 7pm-10pm Tue-Sat, 12.30pm-2.15pm Sun
Closed Xmas
Average Price: dinner £19-£21
Credit Cards: Visa, Access/Mastercard, Amex, Diners
No Service Charge
Restaurant Licence
Wheelchair Access
Children — controlled children welcome
Vegetarian options always available
Skerries is 29km north of Dublin and signposted from the N1 Dublin/Belfast road.
The restaurant is in the centre of town.

ROLY'S BISTRO ➡ £

7 Ballsbridge Terrace, Dublin 4 Tel: (01) 668 2611
Roly Saul, Colin O'Daly

Roly Saul's eponymous restaurant is the greatest success story in Ireland's restaurant culture in recent years, and its success is richly deserved. Indeed, if there is a reward on this earth for initiative, innovation, creativity and professionalism, Mr Saul and his team deserve it more than most.

Their secret has lain with the assembly of the dream team who run the place: John O'Sullivan who handles the paperwork: Roly Saul who masterminds meeting and greeting and the extraordinary business of seating people, a task so complicated he refers to it as "3—D chess".

And the lynch-pin of the team is Colin O'Daly, a chef who has metamorphosed from an intricate, involved cook into a Bistro Barnstormer without the slightest sign of tension.

Mr O'Daly's contribution is to create, demand and insist upon food of a superbly high standard, to insist on correctness of preparation and presentation. For what you get in Roly's — aside from a restaurant space of exquisite elegance and comfort, aside from staff who are dedicated and mindblowingly efficient — is food which is much, much better than you have a right to expect, given the price they charge. Roly's is the best bargain in Irish food, because you get the finest food at the finest price.

And they do not cut corners. There are no shortcuts, no edges trimmed. The food — roasted leg of lamb, game pie with cranberries, chicken niçoise, salmon trout with a fennel and saffron sauce, a smoked fish cake, and a crêpe stuffed with spinach, oyster mushrooms, Swiss cheese and sesame seeds as the vegetarian choice — are typical of the array of main courses offered on a week's menu. All of them will be correctly cooked, and bright and voluptuous with flavour, dishes which fuse slap-happy bistro flavours with a refinement worthy of a brasserie.

Best of all, Roly's is a fun place. No matter whether you are eight or eighty, the secret of Roly's success is that you can extract from it what you want.

Open noon-2.45pm, 6pm-10pm Mon-Sun
Closed Xmas and Good Fri
Average Price: lunch £9.50, dinner £15
Credit Cards: Visa, Access/Mastercard, Amex, Diners
10% Service Charge
Restaurant Licence
Wheelchair Access
Children — no special facilities
Vegetarian options always available
On the corner between Ballsbridge and Herbert Park, just down from the American Embassy.

DESTRY'S

The Square, Clifden, Connemara, Co Galway Tel: (095) 21722
Paddy & Julia Foyle

It was Lord Beaverbrook who said that the sight of Marlene Dietrich, standing on a bar, in black net stockings, belting out "See What The Boys In The Back Room Will Have", in the film "Destry Rides Again" was a greater work of art than the Venus de Milo.

Well, maybe. What is certain is that, whilst Marlene is a greater work of art, Venus is, most likely, the better singer.

Paddy Foyle's admiration of Marlene has extended not just to borrowing the title from the classic western in which she starred with James Stewart, but extended also to borrowing some of the lady's capacity for re-invention. A desire to simplify his food, and to work in a funkier ambience, has led to this splendid place, not too far from his original stomping ground of Rosleague Manor, and just up the hill from his newest invention, the splendid Quay House.

Destry gallops along on good humour, good food and adrenalinated energy. The cooking enjoys Mr Foyle's signature, that intuitive grasp for motivating flavour in a dish and finding unusual alliances. The marinated leg of lamb may seem as untypical an Irish dish as you could imagine — the cubes of meat char-grilled to a rich spiciness and offset by a chutney sauce — but the flavours could be found nowhere else than the west coast. With a Barbary duck, Mr Foyle extracts the full complement of rich flavours, whilst his fish cooking has always proved to be feistily inventive, with clever experiments such as coating white hake in black sesame seeds to produce a dish that dazzles both vision and appetite.

Clifden has needed a place like Destry for a long time: someplace to enjoy 5 Star fish 'n' chips, that perfect somewhere that matches the exuberance of the holidaymaker, somewhere kids just adore, somewhere that pulses with the pleasure of good food and good times. Just imagine if it was called The Venus De Milo. No, just can't imagine it being called The Venus De Milo.

Open noon-10pm Mon-Sun
Closed Nov-Easter
Average Price: lunch £10.50, dinner from £15.50
Credit Cards: Visa, Access/Mastercard
No Service Charge
Wine Licence
Wheelchair Access
Children — always welcome, menus by arrangement
Vegetarian Option served each evening
Clifden town centre.

DRIMCONG HOUSE ★ £

Moycullen, Co Galway Tel: (091) 85115
Gerry & Marie Galvin

"My motivation and my guiding light is to experiment and, being Irish, to try to build on what we have", writes Gerry Galvin in his marvellous book of recipes, recollections and poems, "The Drimcong Food Affair".

Mr Galvin, happily, is a man of action as much as a man of words and, if he is one of the leading intellects and thinkers in the world of Irish food, he is also one of its principal practical exponents.

His experiments are creative and continuous, with each weekly menu drawing new ideas from the chef himself and his team. Typical of the man is the fact that Drimcong has begun over the years to establish itself as a superb training ground for young cooks, and a plenitude of youngsters has emerged from under Mr Galvin's wings to carry off cooking awards and to begin to establish themselves as serious individuals. Teacher as well as preacher.

His dish of black pudding and oysters with an apple and onion confit is already a legend, and he will improvise it into a marvellous black pudding mousse. This touch with rustic, obvious foods, this attempt to heighten and isolate flavours, is found in the Connemara lamb with a mousse of peas and a garlic gravy, in pigeon with couscous and a red wine sauce, in a rabbit and venison pie with a chocolate flavoured sauce, in simple things such as colcannon soup, tipsy pudding, roast pike.

There are marvellous foods for vegetarians — herb and parmesan omelette, polenta and aubergine gâteau — and for children — pan-fried chicken or grilled fish, ice-creams. Whatever one chooses, certain truths emerge about the cooking: it is deeply considered, and very generous in spirit, motivated by a hungry creativity, and it is distinctly Irish. Drimcong House, with its splendid staff and their obvious happiness and pride in their work, its sense of serenity and its respect for the efforts of those who work here and those who eat here, is a magnificent creation.

Open 7pm-9pm Tue-Sat
Closed Xmas-9 Mar
Average Price: dinner £15.95-£18.95
Credit Cards: Visa, Access/Mastercard, Amex, Diners
10% Service Charge
Full Licence
Wheelchair Access (apart from three negotiable steps to hall)
Children — high chairs, children's menu £8.50
Recommended for Vegetarians
Driving on the N59 out of Galway to Clifden, a few miles west of Moycullen, the restaurant is signposted on the right hand side.

CHEF OFF DUTY

ERRISEASKE HOUSE HOTEL & RESTAURANT ★
Ballyconneely, Clifden, Co Galway Tel: (095) 23553 Fax: 23639
Christian & Stefan Matz

Stefan Matz, the quiet, young chef of the Erriseaske, cooks with such a mixture of discipline and daring that his food is truly organic: perfectly formed, perfectly allied, perfectly cooked.

With every dish, he shows a wonderful balance between textures which are ethereal, and tastes which can punch their weight. Home-made gravadlax, the slices of salmon resting on watercress leaves, has a splash of hot mustard in the dill sauce; a lobster salad marinated in a chervil vinegar, whose flavour it had greedily absorbed, has a sweet, clean edge. A slender ravioli is stuffed with a mixture of lobster and mushrooms, with the trump card of a little consommé in the salad dressing.

The same device is used in the dressing of the salad leaves for a millefeuille of sweetbreads, the dish arranged in an architectural delight: a trio of pastry discs made from spring roll pastry cut and baked with egg yolk, then small slices of the sweetbreads interleaved into the little tower of poppadum-thin discs.

A quartette of raviolis — boy, doesn't this guy like raviolis! — one flavoured with tomato and a second with spinach, whilst the others were plain, were respectively stuffed with ricotta cheese, fromage blanc with garlic and onions, spinach, and mushrooms with parsley. Loin of veal with two sauces had been roasted on the bone, but then cut away and the bone left on the plate. The sauces were a light foie gras and an unctuous port and madeira, a startling variation with two of the ingredients in the sauce for the ravioli. A lemon tart whose pastry was of such inestimable thinness that it reminds one of a communion wafer, except here the worthiness is replaced by a melting, crumbling piece of perfection. The Hotel itself has relaxed a little and the dining room is happy with kids and holidaymakers and locals, with Mr Matz's brother Christian overseeing everything with his winning, shy style. Mr Matz's food is nothing less than a drama of exquisite food, some of the finest cooking in Ireland today.

Open 6.30pm-9.30pm Mon-Sun
Closed 1 Nov-1 Apr
Average Price: dinner £21.90
Credit Cards: Visa, Access/Mastercard, Amex, Diners
No Service Charge
Restaurant Licence
No Wheelchair Access
Children — high chairs
Vegetarian menus by arrangement
Take the coast road from Clifden to Ballyconneely, then follow the signposts.

HIGH MOORS RESTAURANT
Dooneen, Clifden, Co Galway Tel: (095) 21342
Hugh & Eileen Griffin

There are certain restaurants, which are just the sort of places you dream of discovering when you are on holiday.

You would like to find someplace where the food had something of a domestic character, indeed where the restaurant itself had a domestic character; almost as if someone was welcoming you into their home.

And you would hope that the food would be simply cooked, quietly expressive of its own tastes and flavours.

And you would hope the service would be serene and calm, for you want, really, a night which begins slowly but then, gradually, takes off, until soon it is sometime in the small hours and that voice you are hearing in that pub singing that song is . . . , eh, well, your voice, actually.

High Moors is the place to kick off an evening like this, a holiday special. It opens at Easter, closes in the autumn, and in between Hugh and Eileen Griffin welcome people into a restaurant which is, in fact, their home. You can look out across the wild, remorseless moors as sunset falls, and await the quiet pleasures of Eileen Griffin's food.

It will be simple food but it will taste delicious, because a lot of it will have been grown by Hugh himself, just a stone's throw down the road. The rest will have been sourced locally, and Eileen knows how to get the best out of it. Brill will have a red pepper and chive sauce; duck breast with a purée of apple, sage and onion. With some of their own gravadlax to begin, and maybe some summer berries and currants in brandy syrup for dessert, you will smile and say that you have found that place you were thinking of. And, then, off to the pub, and that song that beats in your head . . .

Open 6.30pm-9.30pm Wed-Sun
Closed Nov-Apr
Average Price: dinner £12
Credit Cards: Visa, Access/Mastercard, Amex
10% Service Charge
Wine Licence
Wheelchair Access
Children — high chairs and half portions
Varied Vegetarian Menu served each evening
Look for the sign, 1km from Clifden on the Ballyconneely road, directing you to a side road just off the main road.

MAINISTIR HOUSE HOSTEL £
Inis Mór, Aran Islands, Co Galway Tel: (099) 61169 Fax: 61351
Joël d'Anjou

Why is Joël d'Anjou such a good cook?

Simple. Because he is an improviser. He makes it up as he goes along, cooking at all times without knowing precisely what he is going to finish up with. Like a great jazz musician, he takes a theme, then begins to shape it according to his own style. At the end, at the conclusion of the rollercoaster that is dinner in Mainistir, you know only that someone who implicitly, intuitively understands food has melded and moulded basic ingredients into these amazing dishes. But you might not be able to understand just how it has been done.

For no one else cooks like this man. No one else has enough savvy and confidence to simply let things unfold, to trust that it will all work out well. We watched, one summer day, as Jöel used the organic herbs which had just been delivered to the back door, to make an Aran Pesto.

Half a head of garlic and half a salad bowl of hazel-nuts were ground up with a predominance of parsley and basil, but chives, tarragon, coriander, dill, chervil and marjoram were all tossed into the pot with salt and vegetable oil. A far cry from the simplicity of Ligurian pesto, M d'Anjou produced a sauce that walloped you with its freshness, its greenness, its earthiness, its ruddy vitality. He simply made it up as he went along, but you never doubted for an instant that it would be anything other than outrageously good. Which it was.

Cooks, like any artists, are at their best when there is an element of exploration, of uncertainty, in their work, when they are still unsure of how something will finally turn out. That is what makes food interesting, and that is what makes Jöel d'Anjou's hostel, and his cooking, so special. Every dish eaten in the summer's week was special: spicy aubergines with a red onion relish; carrots in an orange sauce; a curry of lentils; mange tout with garlic and crystalised ginger. The cooking, incidentally, is almost exclusively vegetarian. Don't worry. Many other people don't notice it either.

Open for dinner 8pm sharp (7pm winter)
Open all year incl Xmas and New Year
Average Price: dinner £7
Credit Cards: Visa, Access/Mastercard
No Service Charge
No Licence (bring your own)
No Wheelchair Access
Children — welcome
Recommended for Vegetarians
When you arrive on the pier or the airport ask for Mairtin.

O'GRADY'S SEAFOOD RESTAURANT
Market Street, Clifden, Co Galway Tel: (095) 21450
The O'Grady family

For many visitors to the bracingly boisterous resort town of Clifden, O'Grady's Seafood Restaurant is as automatic and as essential a stop as St. Peter's, when in Rome, or Mulligan's bar, when in Dublin.

The business of the O'Grady family has always been to look after people, and they do that by doing their best to help you have a good time, whether you want a simple family lunch, a single plate of food, or a grander dinner to mark the end of a happy holiday.

The food the family serve, an easeful essay on simple ingredients and good flavours, explains the restaurant's enduring success, right from first bite to last.

Everything here is designed to make you feel comfortable, to usher in a relaxed time, to make sure you get the very best out of a meal and out of an evening. The lighting is low, the tables are intimately arranged if you want, socially arranged if you don't, service is charming, and the fillets of fish are fresh, the cuts of meat are flavorful, the bread is good, the desserts are sinfully sweet.

SALMON

Open noon-2.30pm, 7pm-10pm Tue-Sat
Closed Dec-Mar (open Xmas and New Year)
Average Price: lunch £9, dinner £18
Credit Cards: Visa, Access/Mastercard, Amex
No Service Charge
Full Licence
Wheelchair Access to restaurant but not to toilets
Children — over 5yrs welcome
Vegetarian options always available
In the centre of Clifden.

TIGH NEACHTAIN RESTAURANT

2 Quay Street, Galway, Co Galway Tel: (091) 66172/46403
Stephan and Maureen Zeltner-Healy

Perhaps the best way to make your way upstairs to the restaurant in Neachtain's, is to arrive through the main part of one of Galway's most authentic pubs. Tigh Neachtain, in this delightedly frisky part of town known as Galway's "Latin Quarter", is famous not only for good pints but also for good music. It is now getting a name for good food.

This is thanks to Stephan and Maureen Zeltner-Healy. He is the chef, and she is always to be found front of house, amidst the burgundy walls, the open fires and the candle light. Curiously, for somewhere over a pub, Neachtain's has a sort of Country House Parlour atmosphere. It's not very formal: nobody bothers whispering in here, so it's a good place to pick up hot Galway gossip.

There is a table d'hôte, an à la carte and — the most adventurous — a Stephan Special, and they all share excellent value for money.

Mr Zeltner-Healy makes a fine oyster and mussel ragout — sweet seafood in a sauce flavoured with dried mushrooms — and grills marinated lemon sole which is served on top of good lettuce leaves.

His fondness for profound, punchy flavours is best seen in main courses, like grilled loin of venison which comes with a rich date and honey sauce, or roast breast of Barbary duck which is knocked into compliance by a powerful boletus sauce. Vegetables are good, and properly served: no dread kidney plates.

Puddings are enjoyably classical: syrupy pears poached in red wine with a brandy parfait; some tangy stewed berries with mixed parfaits. The wine list is decent and decently priced, and Galway has needed this alliance of good food and great crack for some time.

Open 6.30pm-10.30pm Mon-Sat
Closed 1 week in Nov, Xmas
Average Price: dinner £13.50
Credit Cards: Visa, Access/Mastercard
No Service Charge
Full Licence
No Wheelchair Access
Children — over 5yrs welcome
Vegetarian options always available
On the corner of Cross Street and Quay Street.

QUAY HOUSE ➥ £
Clifden, Co Galway Tel: (095) 21369
Paddy & Julia Foyle, Dermot Gannon

"He is an alchemist", Paddy Foyle will tell you about his young chef, Dermot Gannon.

Mr Foyle is right. Mr Gannon makes a warm salad of mussels and smoked bacon, with an anchovy and soya dressing, in which he deep-fries the mussels in a breadcrumb overcoat, to achieve an effect where the moistness in the shellfish will open into the mouth as you bite through the crisp coating. Alchemy? Addiction! "Every time I come here I want to order something different, and I always order the mussels and bacon" a friend confided.

This is a classic starter, for it awakens the taste buds instantly with adroit, precise tastes, and is so refreshing and clean in flavour that the senses tumble into sublime delight.

With something as up-front as sautéed lamb's kidneys and sweet-breads with a red onion confit, the moist pleasure of the offal is embraced by a confit which is sweet and melting, the sauce teased out with threads of orange zest and black sesame seeds that one mops up with a dynamite red pepper and olive bread.

Like any good cook, Mr Gannon allows main courses to be less effusive than starters, more composed. Fillets of sole are served with a leek sauce that is silky, just so; the sesame crust around grilled pork fillet is smartly green and herby, the meat moist and earthy, a ginger sauce perfectly understated, whilst fresh tagliolini with an escalope of wild salmon is as graceful as goodness itself.

The design of Quay House is quite wondrous. One half of the dining room is a wood pigeon blue, its formality undercut by the fact that those great big round dining tables are coated with paper tablecloths, whilst the other is a breezy, bright, white-washed space, with minimalist, modern lighting, black metal chairs and the colourful splash of a hand-tufted carpet against one wall, and a Plaster-of-Paris bust propped in one window. They should hang a sign outside that says: Alchemists At Work.

Open 7pm-10pm Mon-Sun
Closed Nov-Easter
Average Price: dinner £22
Credit Cards: Visa, Access/Mastercard
No Service Charge
Wine Licence
Wheelchair Access
Children — no facilities
Vegetarian meals with prior notice
At the Bank of Ireland, at the top of the town, take the lower road out of town heading towards the harbour.

BEGINISH RESTAURANT

Green Street, Dingle, Co Kerry Tel: (066) 51588
John & Pat Moore

Pat Moore is a serious cook, and a seriously skilful one. She has already created one of the most talked-about dishes in recent years in Ireland — a hot rhubarb soufflé tart of such ethereal tenderness and drop-dead deliciousness that it hits the senses with the shock of waking from a dream — but there is much more to her skills than those of the talented patissier.

Her cooking reveals a cook who is hungrily inquisitive, her work full of those little gestures which announce the improvisations and experimentations of a cook who wants to learn more and more. One of the greatest errors made by many chefs is their disinterest in the work of their peers. Mrs Moore has not only eaten the food of the great chefs, she is a perceptive critic of the work of even the most luminary individuals, and she knows how to assimilate the strengths of other people's work into her cooking, and how to avoid their shortcomings.

Where this comes most happily into play is in her appreciation for flavour, and the need to locate and capture the integral flavour of an ingredient whilst, at the same moment, contrasting or comforting it with an apposite sauce. With flaky, sweet crab meat, she will combine the shellfish with a chive mayonnaise, whilst tender pinky prawns will have a sharply spiced mayonnaise to play against.

A fillet of turbot will sit on a scrumptious bed of potato purée with a clean chive sauce circling the dish, whilst roasted john dory will have a dazzlingly colourful brunoise of vegetables tapestried around the dish with a creamy mustard sauce perfectly accenting the freshness and liveliness of the fish.

Tastes are very positive and happy, and the sense of balance in the main courses is instinctively judged. There are, of course, the essential nods to Saturday night specials — beef fillet with rostis, spring lamb, Beginish lobster — but fish rightly predominates on the menu: black sole on the bone meuniere; fillet of brill garnished with a julienne of leek. When in Dingle, you want to be in the Beginish. Simple as that.

Open 12.30pm-2.15pm, 6pm-10pm Tue-Sun
Closed mid Nov-mid Mar
Average Price: lunch £2.50-£10, dinner £16
Credit Cards: Visa, Access/Mastercard, Diners
No Service Charge
Full Pub Licence
No Wheelchair Access
Children — welcome
Varied Vegetarian dishes served each evening
Almost opposite the Catholic church, half way up Green Street at the top of the town.

D'ARCY'S

Main Street, Kenmare, Co Kerry Tel & Fax: (064) 41589
Matthew and Aileen d'Arcy

Matt d'Arcy's Old Bank House may be set in somewhat simpler premises than the grandeur of The Park Hotel, his old stomping ground just down the hill in Kenmare where he was head chef for many years, but the rich complexity and lavish culinary control of d'Arcy's cooking are every bit as evident here as before.

"Flawless technique and understated flavours", were the essentials of his style, The New York Times said some years back. More accurately, they said "Some of Mr d'Arcy's combinations are daring". Indeed they are.

His love of variation and complication, of finding new alliances, is rampant throughout an agonising-to-choose-from menu: warm ravioli of prawn mousse with a sweet pepper scented butter; salmon with noodles in a light curry sauce; chicken and noodle soup with star anise; scallops fried in the pan with leeks and grapes. All of this is unexpected, original for an Irish chef, and it makes Mr d'Arcy's dishes endlessly fascinating.

At the same time as one relishes the inventiveness and unexpected-ness, you are also struck by the fact that this cooking, with its impressive architecture of design and concentrated focus of taste, manages to be both classic and, at the same time, very modern. Such intelligent strid-ing across the barriers of taste and the styles of time demands a singular discipline. Matt d'Arcy has it.

The dining room is simple, enjoyable space, perhaps at its best on cool evenings when the fire burns bright, and there is a good bottle of wine to enjoy with this good food.

Open 5pm-10.30pm Mon-Sun (Apr-Oct), 7pm-10.30pm Fri-Sun (Oct-Mar)
Closed Xmas and last week in Jun and first week in Feb
Average Price: dinner £15-£25
Credit Cards: Visa, Access/Mastercard
No Service Charge
Wine Licence
Wheelchair Access
Children — welcome, half portions
Vegetarian meals only with prior notice
At the top end of Main Street, on the left hand side as you drive up the hill.

GABY'S

17 High Street, Killarney, Co Kerry Tel: (064) 32519
Geert & Marie Maes

Gaby's has moved a little bit further up the street from its old location in Killarney but its signature sign — an upturned corrach with three male figures underneath transporting the boat along a shore — means it is easily discoverable.

The signature sign has stayed the same and so has the consistency and effectiveness of Geert Maes' cooking. In a town full of froth and flotsam, and endless menus packed with ersatz food, Mr Maes is a serious cook who knows well what he does best, and this professionalism means that Gaby's is just the sort of restaurant you desperately want to find in Killarney, especially on one of those days when the streets are clogged with human traffic, and you clamour for respite.

The restaurant is almost a café in style, with a bare-boarded European feel. The cooking concentrates on Mr Maes' strength with fish and shellfish: a shellfish platter; black sole in a cream sauce; hot salmon or hot smoked trout; their own secret way of preparing lobster fresh from the tank. It is cooking that is just right for an informal lunch, just right for both a family or a romantic dinner.

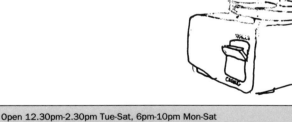

Open 12.30pm-2.30pm Tue-Sat, 6pm-10pm Mon-Sat
Closed Xmas week and Feb
Average Price: lunch £3-£6, dinner £10-£26
Credit Cards: Visa, Access/Mastercard, Amex, Diners
10% Service Charge
Restaurant Licence
Wheelchair Access
Children — high chairs and half portions
Vegetarian meals with prior notice
Killarney Town Centre.

LOAVES & FISHES
Caherdaniel, Co Kerry Tel: (0667) 5273
Helen Mullane & Armel White

They are a good twosome, Helen Mullane and her man Armel White.
Together, they deliver a splendid confection in Loaves & Fishes, making
this one of those places which you dream about finding when you are
travelling or touring, or just plain loafing around.

Ms Mullane sets the tone in front of this intimate house, at just that
right combination of bashful holiday happiness — candlelit tables,
intimate lighting, comforting crooners on the stereo. She is one of the
finest restaurant people in the country: confident, in control, calm as
you would wish you could only be.

Mr White, meantime, takes care of the culinary ambience in Loaves
& Fishes, and the busy sounds of whisking, slicing and sizzling coming
from the little kitchen reassure as to the trueness of the restaurant,
whilst the aromas of something brewing up or reducing down lingeringly
drift out to the dining room, and set the appetite up for the evening.

Mr White's food trades on deep flavours and his aim is to find a
new fusion of tastes by means of unexpected combinations. So he will
mix pork with Parma ham and mozzarella and roast the lot of them;
smoked salmon will be grilled, and then have some warame scattered on
top. In tandem with these experiments there will be a stable of culinary
staples: sirloin with a café de Paris butter; lamb with a honey and thyme
jus; dover sole with a Noilly Prat sauce.

Whatever diversities or delectables he chooses, Mr White proves
himself able to make the dish work, and with some simple but ruddy
vegetables and fine, sticky desserts, you find this food is extremely
enjoyable and companionable. In the context of the romantic, careless
and carefree calm of the restaurant, it is just the food you wanted. Prices
are splendidly modest, and just another part of this charming miracle.

Open 7pm-9.30pm Tue-Sun
Closed Oct-Easter (closed Tue Easter to Jun)
Average Price: dinner £18-£22
Credit Cards: Visa, Access/Mastercard
No Service Charge
Wine Licence
Wheelchair Access (but not to toilet)
Children — no facilities
Vegetarian meals with prior notice
Caherdaniel is on the Ring of Kerry, about 45 mins from Kenmare, 10 mins from
Waterville. Loaves & Fishes is signposted from the main road.

NICK'S RESTAURANT
Lower Bridge Street, Killorglin, Co Kerry Tel: (066) 61219
Nicholas Foley

Crowds and crowds of carefree carousers flock to this cheerful pub-cum-restaurant in the hilly town of Killorglin, meaning that whether or not it is an early Tuesday evening in the middle of a wet September, or maybe a wet Wednesday sometime in early April, Nick's enjoys the celebratory atmosphere of a Friday night wedding.

The food accentuates the festivity of the place, with bumper Saturday night specials like rack of lamb, fillets of fish in creamy sauces and simple, superb steaks from Kerry cattle, all launched at the punters in grand portions and with sweet charm from the ladies who wait on the tables.

To begin the evening, several drinks in the bar of Nick's, as you listen to the whooping choruses belted out on the piano, is imperative before you even consider ordering anything to eat.

Open 12.30pm-3pm, 6.30pm-10pm Mon-Sun
Closed Xmas, Nov, lunch from Sept-Easter, Mon-Tue from Jan-Mar
Average Price: lunch & bar food £4.50-£6, dinner £20-£22
Credit Cards: Visa, Access/Mastercard, Amex, Diners
No Service Charge
Full Bar Licence
Wheelchair Access to restaurant
Children — half portions
Vegetarian stir fry always available
Half way up the hill on the road coming from Tralee or Killarney.

" HAVE YOU A RESERVATION......

PACKIE'S ➥ £

Henry Street, Kenmare, Co Kerry Tel: (064) 41508
Maura Foley

It was a desire to simplify her food, and to cut back on prices, which led Maura Foley to open the smashing venture that is Packie's. This wise foresight — for many others throughout the country have done something similar in recent times — is typical of the same simple genius that you find in her cooking.

Mrs Foley is a brilliant cook, and a modest, ever-learning one, which is how she manages to keep ever-ahead of the posse, a posse who would love to try to filch her ideas, and who would always, but always, get them wrong.

They get them wrong because they don't have Mrs Foley's patience or application, they don't have her sense of culinary balance, her gift for giving delight in a dish. Her food is, we might say, almost maternal, or grand maternal, in nature, a Kerry cuisine-de-grand-mère. You admire it not because it is difficult — for it is not complicated food — but because it is so well done, and because you know that no one else could do it half so well. Only Mrs Foley cooks like Mrs Foley.

And she creates the perfect place in which to eat her food. Packie's is a happy, up-for-it, hot-to-trot place to eat, with great staff, great prices and a wonderful bistro buzz. The foods cooked in here, with their implicit accent on simple flavours, seem almost a revelation, their taste is so real, so true. Scallops with Noilly Prat and mushrooms. Confit of duck. Baked turbot with a seed mustard sabayon. Even time-abused classics like Sole meuniere, or crab claws in garlic butter, have stupendous, fresh, vigorous tastes, and that is before you get around to some spoonsome vanilla ice-cream which will beggar belief it is so fine.

You name it, and you will scarcely be able to remember when you last ate it so good. Don't be surprised, by the way, if you overhear someone at another table using the word "orgasmic". It's not a replay from When Harry Met Sally: it's just someone who is eating here for the first time.

Open 5.30pm-10pm Mon-Sat
Closed end Dec-end Mar
Average Price: dinner £12-£15
Credit Cards: Visa, Access/Mastercard
No Service Charge
Wine Licence
Wheelchair Access (through side door)
Children — high chairs
Recommended for Vegetarians
In the centre of Kenmare.

THE PARK HOTEL
Kenmare, Co Kerry Tel: (064) 41200
Francis Brennan

If one were to hold a poll of hoteliers to find the hoteliers' hotelier, no one would lay a bet with you that the winner would not be Francis Brennan. Mr Brennan is, quite simply, the very personification, the very essence, of the hotelier.

His skills are so effortless and so graceful that you can't imagine that he ever actually learnt them. Far more likely, you reckon, that he was born this way, popped from the womb with this integral and instinctive grasp of how to run an hotel to the very highest standards, and then some.

It is Francis Brennan who personifies and motivates The Park Hotel, articulates its thoughtfulness and appositeness, ensures that the food is correct, that the rooms are perfect, makes it the place it is, makes it like no other place.

It is impossible, then, to divorce this fact from the enjoyment of a meal here. One will admire Brian Cleere's cooking for the harmony and well-tuned balance which he brings to his work and for the simplicity he has introduced to the menu — and the fact that it is now written in English — and one will enjoy fillet of beef with a chartreuse of oxtail, onion confit and a red wine glaze, or a terrine of guinea fowl and pigeon with warm vegetables and truffle vinaigrette, and the superb local fish and shellfish.

But the fine food, the superb service with its magical mix of confidence and friendliness, the great wines — especially the clutch of American wines, many of which can only be found in The Park — is just one part of this brilliant tapestry of pleasure, a tapestry without a single trace of preciousness or snobbery.

Open 1pm-1.45pm, 7pm-8.45pm Mon-Sun
Closed Nov-April (open Xmas period)
Average Price: lunch £18.50, dinner £37
Credit Cards: Visa, Access/Mastercard, Amex, Diners
No Service Charge
Full Pub Licence
Wheelchair Access
Children — high chairs, children's menu, £8
Vegetarian dishes only with prior notice
At the top of the slopes of the village of Kenmare, The Park is well signposted.

SHEEN FALLS LODGE
Kenmare, Co Kerry Tel: (064) 41600
Fergus Moore

Sheen Falls Lodge plights its troth, unambiguously, at high rolling, free-spending travellers, folk with a taste for restrained décor and lavish food. You might find yourself dining alongside visiting foreign royalty in the La Cascade Restaurant, find yourself in the presence of stars and their agents, pulp novelists with healthy current accounts.

If you do, don't worry. Whilst they will be certain to recognise you, they are unlikely to table-hop. The tables are just too far apart, in here.

Fergus Moore's cooking is luxurious in design and execution, but this does not mean that he is a slavish adherent of cuisine Française. He likes to use modern French tricks, it is true, for example by shaking up succulent foie gras by means of the vogueish use of balsamic vinegar, and he will play around with classic ideas, so you might find an alliance of smoked duck breast with deep fried haricots.

The catholicity of choices on the menu allows one to make up an interesting dinner: air-dried beef with capers, tomato and tarragon is intersected with asparagus spears, and that note of tarragon appears again in a fine chicken consommé with mushrooms. The flavours in a rare tuna steak with a ginger and citrus dressing are refreshingly volatile, and it is always a good idea to go for some of the more modish dishes, for they allow the chef to slip off the flavour restraint that can make some dishes just a little too polite.

The staff in the hotel are quite, quite brilliant, and the wine selection superb, though undoubtedly pricey. Some will not like the Sheen Falls, of course, but if you choose carefully you can extract the very best from it, whatever it is you are looking for.

Open 1pm-2pm Sun, 7.30pm-9.30pm Mon-Sun
Closed Jan and Feb
Average Price: Sun lunch £17.50, dinner £37.50
Credit Cards: Visa, Access/Mastercard, Amex, Diners
No Service Charge
Full Licence
Full Wheelchair Access
Children — menus £10-£15
Vegetarian menu always available
One kilometre outside Kenmare, on the Glengarriff road, clearly signed.

THE STRAWBERRY TREE

24 Plunkett Street, Killarney, Co Kerry Tel: (064) 32688
Evan Doyle

Evan Doyle has always been the most perspicacious of restaurant pro-prietors, running the restaurants he has been associated with in pursuit of an ideal of good food, always looking for ways in which to sharpen his focus as to how a restaurant should operate, what food a restaurant should serve in order to acquire its own personality, how he and his staff should work in order to ensure that customers should have a good time.

In The Strawberry Tree, his lovely restaurant in the overheated and often-unlovely town of Killarney, Mr Doyle has taken a brave step into the future, by virtue of an insistence on sourcing all his foods from local, artisan and organic sources. Venison from that dazzlingly talented butcher Armin Weise from Fossa, organic vegetables from Jo Barth which are imported in from County Cork, a job Mr Doyle undertakes himself.

There is free range beef from Thady Crowley, and free range duck and chicken from Barry's farm. Pat Spillane, from just down the street and around the corner, supplies fresh fish and shellfish, and everything has the stamp and signature of its supplier on it.

"Real Foods"is what they call it, and the results can be sublime. Corned beef parcelled in a pouch of cabbage with a parsley sauce inside; fillet of beef chocolate-rich and deep in flavour; melting smoked salmon; herby, sweet mountain lamb. Terrific tastes, and a valuable refuge in Killarney.

Open 6.30pm-10pm Tue Sat (open Mon & Sun in July & Aug)
Closed Jan & Feb (always check times out of season)
Average Price: dinner £20
Credit Cards: Visa, Access/Mastercard, Amex, Diners
No Service Charge
Wine Licence
No Wheelchair Access
Children — high chairs
Vegetarian options always available
Killarney town centre.

TONLEGEE HOUSE ➥
Athy, Co Kildare Tel & Fax: (0507) 31473
Mark and Marjorie Molloy

Here is a good dinner table game to play, especially if you are out on a first date with someone, and you have brought them to dinner at Tonlegee House.

Put your heads together, and think of the great boy-girl double acts in history — Antony and Cleo. Fred and Ginger. Bonny and Clyde. Comden and Green. Yes, okay then, your Mum and Dad, if you must.

Discuss all this in the darkened womb of a room which is the dining room at Tonlegee.

Start with the millefeuille of crab meat with a grain mustard sauce, a beautifully involved creation of Mark Molloy's, ribboned with strips of vegetables and fresh as the sea itself. Okay, Richard and Judy.

Move along with a cracking bowl of cream of celery and blue cheese, into which you spoonishly dip the super breads. Peters and Lee? Come on!

Marjorie Molloy, as you ponder all this, will be getting on with things all around and about you, to the manner born.

Then a breast of guinea fowl, served with a ballotine of its leg, the roast garlic and thyme precise and suitable bedfellows for the rich flesh. Perfect purée of potatoes, crisp leaves of spinach. A beautiful dish.

Fanny and Johnnie, she remembers. The late Fanny and Johnnie.

Out of the choice of desserts, you opt for a crisp, just-right lemon tart with some vanilla ice cream. It has been a perfect dinner.

Depending on just how you are getting on at this point, how confident you are feeling, how much wine you have drunk, you might say: You and Me?

Don't know about that, says your date. But if there is a better double act in the restaurant business than Mark and Marjorie Molloy, I don't know who they are.

Neither do we. Mark and Marjorie. The dream team.

Open 7pm-9.30pm Mon-Thur, 7pm-10.30pm Fri-Sat (Sun nights residents only)
Closed Xmas
Average Price: dinner £20-£22
Credit Cards: Visa, Access/Mastercard
No Service Charge
Full Licence
No Wheelchair Access (though happy to help)
Children — cot, high chair
Vegetarian dishes always available (notice helps)
In Athy, cross two bridges and take the Kilkenny road out of town. Very soon you will see their sign telling you to go left.

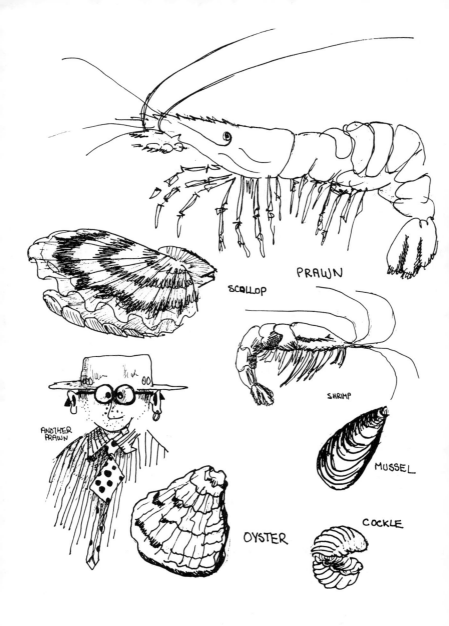

PRAWN

SCALLOP

ANOTHER PRAWN

SHRIMP

MUSSEL

OYSTER

COCKLE

100

LACKEN HOUSE ★

Dublin Road, Kilkenny, Co Kilkenny Tel: (056) 61085 Fax: 62435
Eugene & Breda McSweeney

Invention and tradition. Regionalism and internationalism. The personal and the professional. That diplomat of good food, Eugene McSweeney, brings all these ingredients together in his cooking in this homely, peaceful restaurant with rooms, fusing these competing pressures perfectly into a cuisine which is proud and proudly delicious.

With everything he cooks, Mr McSweeney exploits the long-learnt skill of the professional cook. Skill, here, is used to extract flavour, to reveal the character and essence of a food. Starters such as a warm salad with Dunmore East scallops, or a tartlet of lambs' kidneys in a light mustard sauce, or black pudding on boxty with a sage butter sauce, will taste as good as they can possibly taste. They will taste, quite simply, of themselves.

You will also find that the cooking shows someone who has never lost touch with the scents, attractions and satisfactions of the garden and the ground: a splendid nettle pesto served with a simple vegetable soup; breast of chicken on roasted beetroot; loin of lamb with a tansy mousse. These green, wild tasting of herbs and leaves offer a counterpoint to the luxury of fillet of beef or crispy duckling.

A wise cook, Mr McSweeney keeps his chain of suppliers as short as possible, though he will wander down as far south as Clonakilty to secure Edward Twomey's black pudding in order to make his lively twice-baked black pudding soufflé. Otherwise, everything is local.

And local, also, is the character of Lacken House, the staff are warmly welcoming, and you find the true tastes of Irish food, and Irish hospitality, here. Eugene's wife Breda McSweeney is one of the finest sommeliers in the country, and her expertise is the perfect addendum to her husband's inventiveness and perfectionism.

Open 7pm-10.30pm Tue-Sat
Closed Xmas week
Average Price: dinner £22
Credit Cards: Visa, Access/Mastercard, Amex, Diners
No Service Charge
Restaurant Licence
No Wheelchair Access
Children — high chair and special menu
Recommended for Vegetarians
On the Dublin Road just as you drive into Kilkenny from the north, just past the roundabout.

THE MOTTE
Inistioge, Co Kilkenny Tel: (056) 58655
Alan Walton & Tom Reade-Duncan

As a restaurant, Alan Walton and Tom Reade-Duncan's The Motte makes consummate, charming sense.

Its carefully confected sense of contrivance makes for a pleasingly timeless space that appears to be just exactly how you want a restaurant dining room to appear to be, when you are out for that special night.

Drapes tumble and flow to the ground, and shudder up to the ceiling. The art on the wall is striking, full of presence. The music is stagey and whacky. Gleaming glasses gleam. Linen is crisp and tactile. You have only been in five minutes and already you wish you were Lorenz Hart, and could set about the business of writing a list song in homage to the place.

Alan and Tom like to tinker and toy with tastes, like to twist conventional cooking slightly awry, so calf's liver can come perhaps sweet and sour, perhaps with grilled pineapple; Barbary duck meets audaciously with a black bean sauce, fusing both the great French and Chinese expertise with the dish; swordfish is served with a sauce of red wine, mint and olives.

It is all good fun, this playfulness with contrasts and confections, though they are considerate, also, for those who prefer straightforwardness, so there will be stuffed quail with a spicy onion sauce, a t-bone steak with a garlic, mushroom and artichoke sauce, a simple chicken fillet on a bed of spinach and bacon with a white wine sauce. Desserts opt simply for blow-me! deliciousness: sticky profiteroles, a fine white chocolate cheesecake, all terrifically moreish.

Alan and Tom orchestrate the controlled waywardness of The Motte perfectly, to make a charming evening in a charming restaurant in a charming village.

As we go to press Tom and Alan have told us that they have planning permission to build a new restaurant 500 yards outside the village, overlooking the river. It is intended that the whole shebang will move over an autumn weekend and the restaurant will be the same in style, except for the addition of a couple more tables.

Open 7pm-9.30pm Wed-Sun (open Tue Jun-Sept)
Closed Xmas and bank holidays
Average Price: dinner £18.90
Credit Cards: Visa, Access/Mastercard, Amex
No Service Charge
Wine Licence
Wheelchair Access, but not to toilets
Children — no facilities
Vegetarian dinner with 24 hours prior notice
In the village of Inistioge.

THE MUSTARD SEED

Adare, Co Limerick Tel: (061) 396451
Daniel Mullane

There is a simple answer to the public relations and culinary difficulties which bedevil County Limerick.

Celebrated as somewhere which is unlikely to detain the traveller and the travelling eater overlong, Limerick should — tomorrow — appoint Mr Daniel Mullane as President and Main Man of the county. His seal of office will allow him carte blanche to improve the quality of life in this strange, strangely bourgeois county.

Mr Mullane's qualification for ascending to the job is, simply, that he runs a restaurant — The Mustard Seed — which is not just one of the best in the country, but which, in its thoughtful, considered, creative way of working, shows every other place in Limerick up for the hole-in-the-wall joints they are.

He will solve the matter of crime by using the same charm with which he suffuses his restaurant: no one could cause trouble under the gaze of Mr Mullane's ministrations. He will attend to the matter of the county's less than picturesque towns and villages by designing them to look as much like Adare as possible, for Adare is heartbreakingly lovely. Any difficulty with bureaucrats, roads, water and so on will be solved by the efficiency which Mr Mullane and his chef, Michael Weir, attend to every business.

Mr Weir cooks impressively for vegetarians — a mélange of roasted vegetables on a base of tomato tagliatelle with a roast pimento sauce; twice baked spinach and Gruyère soufflé with lasagne of garden vegetables on a tomato purée — and for the carnivorous: scrambled eggs and panfried lamb's kidneys in a Madeira jus; braised oxtail served with its own gravy and turned vegetables; paupiettes of baked sole with a mousse of crab and spring onion on a bed of panfried scallops. Inventive, individual cooking, but food that never looses off its notes of comfort and homeliness.

Open 7pm-10pm Tue-Sat
Closed Xmas
Average Price: dinner from £25-£27
Credit Cards: Visa, Access/Mastercard, Amex, Diners
No Fixed Service Charge
Restaurant Licence
Wheelchair Access to restaurant, but not to toilets
Children — no facilities
Recommended for Vegetarians
In the centre of Adare village opposite the Dunraven Arms pub.

JORDAN'S PUB & BISTRO

Newry Street, Carlingford, Co Louth Tel & Fax: (042) 73223
Harry and Marian Jordan

Harry and Marian Jordan describe their cooking as "parochial", but don't imagine that this amounts to nothing more than parish pump food. Parochial, here, means the best the parish can offer: tamed oysters from Carlingford Lough and wild samphire from its salt marshes, puddings laced with the local, succumbingly delicious Tyrconnell whiskey, local mushrooms.

In genuine bistro fashion they sometimes offer crubeens and fish'n-'chips, both fancified somewhat: the trotters boned and stuffed, the fish an elegantly poached monk tail with deep fried julienne of turnip. With County Louth typicity, everything is served with a generous spirit, clever but never too serious and the happy style of the food colludes charmingly with this disarmingly seductive village. So seductive, indeed, that it inspired Myrtle Allen to write these lines in "The Irish Times":

"Should I be asked to choose one of the most delectable meals in Ireland, I would say: 'Book a table by the window in Harry Jordan's upstairs dining room on a fine evening. Here one can look out over his little back yard, across the road to King John's Castle and beyond to watch the boats in the waters of Carlingford Lough with the Mountains of Mourne behind. Order freshly gathered Ferguson's oysters, chilled and served simply with lemon and with a selection of Jordan's wonderful breads.'

What a heavenly dream . . ."

Open 12.30pm-2.30pm Sun, 6.30pm-10pm Tue-Sun (early bird menu summer months)
Closed Xmas and 2 wks in Jan & Nov
Average Price: dinner £10-£20
Credit Cards: Visa, Access/Mastercard, Amex.
No Service Charge
Full Licence
No Wheelchair Access
Children — welcome
Vegetarian meals with prior notice
Centre of Carlingford.

ECHOES

Main Street, Cong, Co Mayo Tel: (092) 46059
Siobhan, Tom & Helen Ryan

Whilst Siobhan Ryan garners most of the attention in Echoes — quite rightly, for she is the person who devises the dishes and is the instrumental force in getting them from stove to table — she could not do so without her Dad, who takes care of all manner of supplies to the restaurant, and young Tom, the brother, who is not only an award-winning butcher, but also not above hopping into the kitchen to rattle the pots and pans when Siobhan takes a deserved break.

Siobhan's sister brings to the job of waiting on table a feline grace and a skill which turns her work into an art form. Finally, Siobhan's mother, who welcomes you, organises the bills and cooks breakfast in the restaurant during the summer months, completes this extraordinary picture. It's a family affair.

Together, the family all work to the benefit of the fine food you can expect in Echoes: home-smoked wild salmon on top of a springy bed of crisp salad leaves; breaded monkfish between slabs of green bacon and onions and peppers; fat scallops in a mornay sauce served on the shell surrounded by piped potato; sweet mountain lamb; ice-creams which are the stuff you scream for in your dreams.

At some time in the future someone, with enough time on their hands, will sit down and count the number of times the superlative "Excellent!" — always accompanied by an exclamation mark — appears in the visitors' book to describe Siobhan Ryan's cooking.

Amidst the endless parade of "Excellents!" there appears the heartfelt plea: "Could you post me the recipe for brown bread ice cream?". If you can resist that as a recommendation, then you are made of stern stuff. Those made of less stern stuff will simply melt with joy at this cool, boozy dessert.

This deeply comforting food, full of odoriferous scents and rich with goodness, comes in grandly generous portions, and the happy family affair of Echoes is as far removed from the self-conscious sense of denial that pervades Mayo as you could imagine.

Open 5pm-10pm Mon-Sun (shorter hours during winter season).
Open all year (limited hours Oct-Apr)
Average Price: dinner £14-£19
Credit Cards: Visa, Access/Mastercard, Amex
No Service Charge
Restaurant Licence
Wheelchair Access
Children — high chairs and special menus
Vegetarian options always available
Echoes is right in the centre of Cong, next to the butcher's.

CROMLEACH LODGE

Ballindoon, Castlebaldwin, Boyle, Co Sligo Tel: (071) 65155 Fax: 65455
Christy and Moira Tighe

Cromleach Lodge is a monument to painstaking application. Neither Christy nor Moira Tighe have a background in the business of running a restaurant with rooms, but their determination to improve, their will to succeed, has meant that Cromleach has steadily, steadily built an impressive reputation over the last years.

Moira Tighe's cooking exploits two central commands.

Firstly, she uses impeccable ingredients from local growers, the bulk of the vegetables and herbs being organically grown.

Secondly, thanks to being self-taught, and retaining the modesty which this gives a chef, her cooking strides confidently between transgressive improvisations — one of her best known dishes is a sausage of chicken mousse and crab, for example, served with a deliciously sweet carrot and Sauternes sauce — and the classic verities which she is able to present as if newly invented: beef fillet with a blue cheese sauce; stuffed quail with a pine nut glaze; a duet of salmon and turbot with a tomato compote; escalopes of veal on a grain mustard sauce. Timeless dishes and, here, vitalised by a creative kitchen.

Mrs Tighe admires the work of Anton Mosimann and other modern masters, and she loves bold colour and the intricate assembly of food on every plate. Nowhere more so than with desserts, which are a speciality of Cromleach: warm caramelized pineapple with an orange and honey glaze; barrels of local organic raspberries with a fruit coulis; a terrine of two chocolates with pistachio nuts. The sweet things in life, and how sweet to enjoy them here.

Open 7pm-9pm Mon-Sat, 6.30pm-8.30pm Sun
Closed 23 Dec-21 Jan
Average Price: dinner £29.50
Credit Cards: Visa, Access/Mastercard, Amex
No Service Charge
Restaurant Licence
Wheelchair Access only with assistance
Children — over 7yrs welcome
Vegetarian meal with prior notice
Signposted from Castlebaldwin on the N4, 8 miles north west of Boyle.

GLEBE HOUSE

Collooney, Co Sligo Tel: (071) 67787
Brid and Marc Torrades

Brid Torrades has a skilfulness and an independence in her cooking which we might, perhaps, describe as Olneyesque.

Just as that great culinary master Richard Olney — one of the most celebrated and cultish figures in the world of food — is renowned for his ability to transform foods out of their original context, and to present them as if reborn, Mrs Torrades has the ability to take something simple — cabbage, for heaven's sake! — and, by virtue of shredding it and tossing it and dressing it with a little cream, you have a dish which is unbelievably pure, and gloriously unexpected. If this is cabbage, you say, then what is everyone else doing to it?

But Mrs Torrades can do this with all manner of food. And she does it subtly, quietly. Glebe is a modest, shoe-string operation — they have got the money to improve the kitchen this year — so there are no histrionics, no flamboyance. Her imprimaturs — seasonality, self-sufficiency, clawing in as much local and, indeed, wild food as possible — guarantee food which is drenched with flavour. She is happy to accept the description of a customer, who just happened to be a French chef, that her style of cooking is "Cuisine Bourgeois", and further defines her food as "very simple cooking. Simple and simply decorated, and you cook the food available at the time. Simplicity is the thing". Richard Olney might have said those very words.

This simplicity means that mussels in breadcrumbs with garlic butter will be perfect; fillet of beef with a green peppercorn sauce is cooked appositely in the French way, which means it melts in the mouth; chicken with a basil cream sauce both voluptuous and energetic. Some things may not work, but these are always the exception to a rule of successful, understated cooking. Salads and vegetables, from the garden, are bursting with flavour; sauces are spot on.

Summertime food in Glebe dances with fresh flavours, whilst autumn and winter cooking is consoling and comforting.

Open from 6.30pm-9.30pm Mon-Sun (light lunches in summer from 1pm)
Closed 2 weeks in Jan and Mon & Tue in winter
Average Price: dinner £16.25
Credit Cards: Visa, Access/Mastercard, Amex
No Service Charge
Wine Licence
Wheelchair Access (to restaurant, but not toilets)
Children — high chairs, menu £8
Vegetarian meal always available
Signposted in Collooney, just before the bridge as you drive westwards out of the village towards Sligo.

TRUFFLES ★
11 The Mall, Sligo, Co Sligo Tel: (071) 44226
Bernadette O'Shea

"Pizza? What an odd, ordinary thing for one of America's most respected establishments to put on the menu, even in its relaxed café upstairs. When the pizza came and I tasted it, I saw what Alice Waters was about: the ordinary made extraordinary by the use of fine unusual ingredients... put together by a skilful and unusual taste".

This is the late, great Jane Grigson describing her first visit to the pizza café which the renowned American cook Alice Waters runs upstairs in her restaurant Chez Panisse, in San Francisco. Mrs Grigson might have been writing for the thousands who have had a similar, equally epiphanous experience, in Bernadette O'Shea's restaurant, Truffles, in Sligo town.

"The ordinary made extraordinary". The ability to imagine and then enact an alchemical culinary brilliance is what sets Ms O'Shea apart. You don't eat her food and think: what a shame this lassie doesn't try something else and see how well she could do it, something serious.

Instead, you bite into the perfect alliance of light, essential dough and savour the startling succulence of the assembled ingredients and you realise, then, that you are eating food which is perfect.

How is it perfect? Because it is conceived and executed as a totality: this is pizza as total food: pizza as a template for organic tastes: pizza as a springboard for "fine unusual ingredients", pizza as an expression of great cooking skill and creativity. And it must be stated that Ms O'Shea brooks no compromise when it comes to making pizza, least of all when it comes to her own commitment and involvement. To watch her at work is to see a great artist moving confidently about her métier: the graceful rhythm, the intuitive grasp of colour and taste contrast; the split-second timing, the breathless delivery, the joy in her art.

You get great cooking in Truffles, and everything else to match: great fun, good wines, the coolest staff, the very best time. Jane Grigson would have loved it.

Open 5pm-10.30pm Tue-Sat
Closed Xmas
Average Price: dinner £10
No Credit Cards
No Service Charge
Wine Licence
Wheelchair Access (but not to toilets or wine bar)
Children — welcome
Recommended for Vegetarians
The Mall is an extension of Stephen's Street, on the main Enniskillen road, going towards Sligo General Hospital.

CHEZ HANS

Cashel, Co Tipperary Tel: (062) 61177
Hans Peter & Jason Matthias

"Thank you, Lord, for preserving me to eat another dinner at Chez Hans", intones the jowly, prelate-perfect man who had, clearly, strolled out of the pages of G.K. Chesterton.

He speaks for us all.

With the image of the Last Supper staring down at you, with its poignant bitterness, the fact that Chez Hans was formerly a church makes it the perfect place to break bread, especially in the company of prelate-perfect types. Its secret lies with its magical ability, despite twenty-five years of business, to make every evening seem like a first night. The staff are sweet and keen and professional, and only the music leaves anything to be desired: with that vaulting roof and the sun-comprehending glass, you tend to want to hear Bach cantatas, so getting some dithery diddledy-eye is disappointing.

Jason Matthias' food is punchy and sustaining, almost old-fashioned. A red pepper and roasted artichoke soup is direct and power-ful in flavour, perfect with the superb pumpernickle bread they serve. Quail with wild mushrooms will be perfectly roasted and will have achieved that glorious, irresistible richness which forces you to eat the birds with your fingers. This is unapologetically sumptuous food.

Vegetables in Chez Hans are, it seems, prepared for someone who is girding themselves to gather winter wheat by hand: mounds of spicy champ, a lather of crisp carrots, lots and lots of broccoli, a drumlin of creamy mushrooms. They don't gather the winter wheat by hand in Tipperary anymore but, clearly, no one has told them that in Chez Hans.

A perfect Cointreau-flavoured soufflé with a kiwi sauce will counterpoint all this indulgence with its effete precision. And then, like all the happy families and couples and clerics, with their well-fed smiles and their contented relaxation, you will mutter "Thank you, Lord, for preserving me to eat another dinner at Chez Hans". The prelate-perfect man out of the pages of G.K. Chesterton said it. Everyone thinks it.

Open 6.30pm-9.30pm Tue-Sat
Closed last 3 weeks in Jan
Average Price: dinner £22
Credit Cards: Visa, Access/Mastercard
No Service Charge
Full Licence
Wheelchair Access
Children — no facilities
Vegetarian Menu served only on prior arrangement
Just beside the Rock of Cashel, and clearly signposted from the Dublin-Cork road as you come into Cashel going south.

DWYER'S OF MARY STREET
5 Mary Street, Waterford, Co Waterford Tel: (051) 77478
Martin Dwyer

Martin Dwyer likes to cook, enjoys the business of cooking for people, and it shows. His food is very pleasing to eat, thanks to interesting and considered variations in texture and colour, and clever relocations with certain ingredients.

Lettuce and sorrel soup is a fine signature dish, and that sorrel can turn up again in an onion sauce to partner local salmon. His fish cooking is very strong, and he will accentuate the rich taste of monkfish by wrapping it in a herb crust and serving it with tapenade.

Garlic prawns in a rosti nest — a smart rejigging of something that might be more usually found at home in a Chinese restaurant — is another signature dish of a cook who comfortably walks that line between food which maintains his own interest — by virtue of presenting himself with a changing culinary challenge, and by continually introducing new foods and new tastes — and who can manage to make this food seem comforting and accessible to a somewhat cautious clientele.

But not too cautious, a clientele, it should be said. Mr Dwyer has built a devoted following in Waterford since moving here.

Mr Dwyer has built this rapport with his audience by slowly bringing them along with him as he has matured and developed as a cook, gradually getting them more involved in the evolution of Dwyer's, making them eager for more exciting dishes. At the same time, cleverly, he has always maintained those twin pillars of cooking which is both considerate and honest.

The restaurant itself is a molly-coddling sort of space, tucked away in a quiet street not too far from the waterfont. Good service and a good wine list has helped his impressive championing of serious food in the town, and the combination of an almost-maternal care, soft music and good food is quite charming.

Open 6pm-10pm Mon-Sat
Closed Xmas, bank holidays and 2 wks in Jul
Average Price: dinner £18-£19 (£13 "early bird")
Credit Cards: Visa, Access/Mastercard, Amex, Diners
No Service Charge
Restaurant Licence
Wheelchair Access
Children — half portions
Vegetarian food served with prior notice
Waterford town centre, 200yds south of the bridge.

OPUS 1
18 High Street, Waterford, Co Waterford Tel: (051) 57766
Michael Quinn

Michael Quinn has a restless, hungry culinary character. His background in food is rock solid — he rattled the pots and pans on the stoves in Ballymaloe House, in County Cork, in recent times — but even there he took time out to see the goings on of fine chefs such as Simon Hopkinson in London and Shaun Hill in Devon, and to pick up the tricks of a smart food operator such as Anthony Worrall-Thompson.

His cooking in his brand-new restaurant in High Street, which cheekily adapts the name of the famous wine made collaboratively by Robert Mondavi and Baron Philippe de Rothschild, shows a cook eager to extend his education in Ballymaloe. "I cook the stuff I like cooking — it's sort of salady, tasty food that won't break the bank. It's healthy", he says.

It's also fun: fine bruschetta with herbed mushrooms, olives, sun-dried tomatoes and Parmesan cheese; a soulful leek and potato pie served with salads and crispy bacon; a great lunchtime dish of mixed bean stew with butcher's sausages and buffalo chips.

This is zappy, up-front cooking, and main courses maintain this devotion to flavour: chicken breast with ginger, lemon, rocket and cherry tomatoes; char-grilled sirloin of beef with rosemary, olive oil and french fried onions; pan fried wild mallard breast with a forest mushroom and juniper berry sauce; warm water prawns with a tomato, chilli and coriander salsa. Not just good food, but accessible, satisfying, welcoming food, food that you find you want to eat morning, noon and night.

And does the wine list include Opus One? Well, go to Opus 1 and you will see . . .

Open noon-2.30pm, 6.30pm-10pm Mon-Sat
Closed Xmas and bank holidays
Average Price: lunch £5, dinner £15-£20
Credit Cards: Visa, Access/Mastercard
No Service Charge
Wine Licence
Wheelchair Access (one small step)
Children — welcome
Recommended for Vegetarians
High Street runs parallel to the Quay in Waterford town centre. Take the turn off heading towards the new city square car park.

WATERFORD CASTLE
The Island, Ballinakill, Co Waterford Tel: (051) 78203
Paul McCluskey

Though Waterford Castle is an unapologetic bourgeois stomping ground, one of those places which seems to have been built to congratulate the ego, and flatter the capacious wallets, of the wealthy, you should not allow this to blind you to the fact that Paul McCluskey's food is worthy of anyone's attention.

Mr McCluskey's cooking is both innovative and thoughtful: smoked quail and duck with fennel and baby corn plays teasingly with a variety of flavours, but the chef's consideration and care makes sure that it works. Veal with prunes is a fun contrast between toothsome veal and rich prunes, again showing how this chef likes to stamp dishes with his own interpretation, a trick he pulls off again with the inspired revision that is salmon rolled in oatmeal, served on a ginger sauce.

Peripheral and essential matters such as breads, wines, service, and very creative vegetarian pastas, all under-pinned by the certainty of impeccable ingredients, add up to a quiet tour-de-force. Never mind that high falutin' nature of the castle: come here for Mr McCluskey's cooking, and you will have eyes for nothing more than what is on the plate and what is in the glass. And what is sitting across the table, of course.

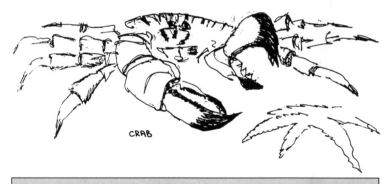

CRAB

Open 12.30pm-2.30pm, 7pm-10pm Mon-Sun
Open all year incl Xmas
Average Price: lunch £16, dinner £33
Credit Cards: Visa, Access/Mastercard, Amex, Diners
No Service Charge
Full Licence
Wheelchair Access
Children — high chairs
Recommended for Vegetarians
Some three miles outside Waterford town, on the Dunmore East road and well signposted. The ferry to the island runs continually.

CROOKEDWOOD HOUSE

Crookedwood, Mullingar, Co Westmeath Tel: (044) 72165
Noel and Julie Kenny

Noel and Julie Kenny's restaurant occupies a vital role in the quixotic midlands of the country, where the flatlands of Dublin and Meath quickly expire in the rush of lake water, and the topographical ruggedness which signals that you are, suddenly, making your way into the west of the country.

Mr Kenny's skills are diverse and his cooking is richly sensuous. He trained for a time in Germany and, whilst some might consider this a distinctly ambiguous pedigree — rather like accusing some one of having a German sense of humour — Mr Kenny seems to have learnt there the ability to fuse powerful flavours with delicate ingredients.

You see this at work when he mixes pasta with shellfish — mussels with fettucine, maybe prawns laced with Pernod to accompany the starchy staple — and the delicate plainness of the pasta is greedily counterpointed by the sweet, punchy shellfish.

The Mitteleuropean influence comes right to the fore when he utilises the wonderful local venison, and serves it in a gulyas with that rare and disarming staple that is spatzle. He will also, intriguingly, pair the game with wild duck in a red wine sauce, a rich and sinuous creation, and combine a honey-roasted pork steak with salmon in filo, serving it with two sauces for an unusual surf 'n' turfer.

This is clever cooking, with the intelligence used to achieve pure, comforting tastes. The sense of comfort which the Kennys want you to enjoy runs right through the evening in Crookedwood: service and ambience and comfort make for a memorable experience.

Open 7pm-10pm Tue-Sat, 12.30pm-2.30pm Sun
Closed Xmas and bank holidays
Average Price: set dinner £18.50, Sun lunch £12
Credit Cards: Visa, Access/Mastercard, Amex, Diners
No Service Charge　　Full Licence
Wheelchair Access (happy to help)
Children — welcome, half portions
Vegetarian options always available
Coming from Mullingar, turn right at the hospital on the road to Castlepollard, then drive to Crookedwood village. Turn right at the Wood pub, then one and a half miles further along you will see the house.

THE WINEPORT RESTAURANT

Glassan, Athlone, Co Westmeath Tel: 0902) 85466
Ray Byrne & Jane English

You can't help but be knocked sideways by the charm of everyone at The Wineport. You can't help but be delighted by how hard they work, how keen they are to please, how determined they are that you should have a good time.

Everybody loves it; young and old, rich and otherwise, couples and families, golfers, sailors, those who hate golf and sailing. It is a charming place, simple as that.

They provide menus for just about everyone: Brunch for late Sunday, with duck liver salad, cod fillet with a basil and pine nut sauce; buckwheat and vegetable pies, perhaps a traditional Sunday roast.

For the kids there will be ham 'n' mushroom pizza, small portions of soup, ice-cream cones. For golfers there are late afternoon menus: steamed mussels; pan-fried sirloin steak; stir-fried chicken and vegetables.

For those who pursue good food without the interruption of needless sporting behaviour, the menu is welcomingly balanced: baked goat's cheese and oven-dried tomatoes with a walnut and herb vinaigrette; a terrine of smoked salmon with a yogurt and chive cream; sole on the bone stuffed with prawns and crabmeat; ravioli filled with spinach and cheese with a tomato and basil sauce finished with shavings of Parmesan. Honest, achievable, fine tasting food.

The Wineport sits hard on the inner lakes of Lough Ree, and can even be reached by boat. Inside, it is a democratic ideal, a charming all-hands-on-deck place, and a winning success.

FRENCH FRIES

POMME FRIT

CHIPS

Open 12.30pm-2.30pm Sun, 6pm-10pm Mon-Sun (open noon-10pm high season)
Closed Xmas
Average Price: lunch £5-£10, dinner £12.50-£20
Credit Cards: Visa, Access/Mastercard, Amex, Diners
No Service Charge
Full Licence
Wheelchair Access (happy to help)
Children — welcome
Recommended for Vegetarians
3 miles north of Athlone, leave the by-pass at exit 4, towards Glassan. Access by boat also.

EUGENE'S RESTAURANT ★ £

Ballyedmond, Co Wexford Tel: (054) 89288
Eugene & Elizabeth Callaghan

In the somewhat unlikely setting of Ballyedmond village — a clatter of
thatched cottages, some new bungalows, a couple of shops, kids on bikes
and gangly dogs, all of it on a road that winds from nowhere to noplace
special — Eugene Callaghan cooks some of the finest food you will find
in Ireland. Not only is it some of the finest food, but it is food that you
would be happy to eat every day of your life. No contrivance, no indulgence, just pure flavours brought to life by a great talent.

On occasion, the cooking in Mr Callaghan's restaurant seizes
flavours which allow things to taste not just of themselves, but also of
where they come from. The agreeable climate of the Sunny South-East
makes for good food. Mr Callaghan takes these good foods, and adds the
final mysterious magic to transform the good food into great cooking.

His eponymous restaurant sits beside a pub, with a take-away
sandwiched in the middle, and it is in this trio of establishments that he
cooks not just for the restaurant but also for the bar — summer salad
with asparagus; fillets of plaice with a chive sauce; a selection of seafood
with a parsley and garlic butter — and, indeed, for the chipper, where he
batters the cod and fries the chips.

The dining room of the restaurant itself is a simple, four-square
space, pastel-quiet, with enough tables to seat thirty or so. The fact that
this space leads you to expect little adds to the delight when the food this
young man can conjure arrives. His dish of braised shank of lamb with
root vegetables has acquired legendary status in just a single year,
acclaimed for its almost elemental, ageless tastes. But the shank of lamb
is not alone: all of the dishes Mr Callaghan cooks are infused and suffused
with clatteringly delicious tastes, and it is purest agony to decide just
what it is you will order: sauté sea scallops with creamed lentils? breast
of chicken with sauté potatoes, leeks and mushrooms? crispy duck
confit with a port sauce? The agony, mercifully, doesn't last long.

Open 12.30pm-2.15pm Mon-Sun, 7pm-9.30pm Mon-Sun (closed Tues evenings).
Closed Xmas
Average Price: lunch £9.50, dinner £14.50
Credit Cards: Visa, Access/Mastercard, Amex, Diners
No Service Charge
Full Licence
Wheelchair Access (but not to toilets)
Children — welcome, but no special menu
Vegetarian options always available
Ballyedmond is on the R741 between Gorey and Wexford.

CURTLESTOWN HOUSE COUNTRY RESTAURANT
Enniskerry, Co Wicklow Tel: (01) 282 5083
Colin & Teresa Pielow

Like somewhere that knows that this year's fancies are passing fancies, someplace that loves the moonlight, a house that loves those old fashioned things — the sound of rain on a window pane, the sorry song that April sings — Colin and Teresa Pielow's Curtlestown House behaves in that old-fashioned way.

Walls in echoingly dark colours and flickering warm fires conspire in a timeless embrace of grandeur and, together, they make you feel good, make you feel welcome, as the ceremony of dinner gets under way. And ceremony is the word: soups are brought in tureens for tables to help themselves, and every dish is attractively confected, as well as generous. Elsewhere, the sort of dinner party ambience which Curtlestown engenders might prove to be killingly twee, but here it is just another aspect of a very innocent, old fashioned thing.

A jamboree of flavours runs right through the ceremony of dinner: smoked salmon is good, and so is Caviston's smoked duck with a hazelnut dressing; lamb is fine and sweet, silverside of corned beef has a parsley sauce which is just right, and vegetables are jam-packed with flavour. Puddings are playful nursery productions — chocolate choux buns with banana cream, apple and blackberry crumble — somewhat typical, in fact, of food which is enjoyably restrained and modest, clubbable grub in the old fashioned way, but with none of the depredations of the old Irish way of doing things.

Open 8pm-10pm Tue-Sat, 12.30pm-2.30pm Sun
Open all year, incl Xmas lunch
Average Price: lunch £12, dinner £18
Credit Cards: Visa, Access/Mastercard
No Service Charge
Wine Licence
Limited Wheelchair Access
Children — Sun lunch only, menu £7
Vegetarian meals with prior notice
Leave Enniskerry on the Glencree Road, up Kilgarron Hill and the restaurant is on the left 2.5 miles along, and brightly lit.

THE OLD RECTORY
Wicklow, Co Wicklow Tel: (0404) 67048 Fax: 69181
Paul & Linda Saunders

Linda Saunders began cooking "Floral Dinners" three years ago in The Old Rectory. "It was an obvious thing to do", Mrs Saunders says. "You start with the herb flowers, and then I simply did more research". Today, she is the leading authority on the use of edible flowers in Ireland, a fount of practical and whacky information — "Culpepper says that Herb Robert is proof against venereal disease" — and mistress of an artform which fuses an elfin delicacy of execution with an intense regard for pure, natural flavours.

Her skill is best illustrated in the 10-course Floral Dinners which they host every so often in The Old Rectory. They are terrific events, but it should be stressed that they are merely an adjunct of this autodidactic cook's repertoire. But what an adjunct!

A menu might begin with Smoked Salmon Parcels with Chive Florets — delicate as a Vuitton valise — and bright yellow Kale Flowers filled with Smoked Salmon Pâté. A herb consommé is lifted by a pot-pourri of herbs — parsley, chervil, sweet cicely, sage, fennel and chives — and the lacing of Silver Birch wine is matched by the same wine in the glass. Glazed Poussin is decorated with herb Robert and pak choi flowers, giving a purple, yellow and green panorama of colour, then a Floral Crêpe with Borage, filled with baby asparagus spears, the flowers pressed directly into the crêpe as it cooks, giving an effect which suggests the dish has been embroidered with herbs, draws a stunned silence from the room of diners.

A brochette of sage accompanies a fine symphony of seafood, then there is salad with a lovely melody of leaves and little quail's eggs, then variegated nasturtiums whose flowers are filled with Cashel Blue cheese and, then, served with a sweet late picked Muscat from Australia, there is croquembouche filled with a rose cream and served with frosted rose petals, a dessert as light as breath and which disappears on the tongue. Finally, a plate of petits fours with candied primroses. Amazing.

Open 8pm Sun-Thurs, 7.30pm-9pm Fri-Sat
Closed Nov-Mar
Average Price: table d'hôte dinner £25
Credit Cards: Visa, Access/Mastercard, Amex, Diners
No Service Charge
Wine Licence
No Wheelchair Access
Children — welcome
Recommended for Vegetarians
30 miles south of Dublin (45 mins), on the left hand side of the road as you enter Wicklow town, heading South.

TINAKILLY HOUSE
Rathnew, Co Wicklow Tel: (0404) 69274
William & Bee Power

If one could fairly say that it is ambition which sets Tinakilly apart from other hotels — an ambition which makes them try harder, strive to achieve more, continue to put pressure on themselves to improve — then one has to say that nowhere throughout the hotel is this more evident than in the kitchen.

John Moloney's cooking is mightily impressive, and it is impressive to one and all. If you like the sweet satisfying and simple flavours of roasted meats and poached fish, then you will be comforted and delighted by his work: steamed fillets of lemon sole with beurre blanc and dill; fillet of beef with champ and a thyme and black peppercorn jus; warm tipsy pudding with mulled wine and honey ice-cream. Spoon licking stuff.

If you want to find something closer to the cutting edge, then you will find it here also. This is an impressive double act for a restaurant to pull off, especially an hotel restaurant which faces extra demands. Mr Moloney and his sous chef, Philip Brazil, do it without blinking.

They can orchestrate the contents of their gourmet dinners as smartly as Busby Berkeley. A fresh lobster salad with a raspberry vinaigrette has the shellfish splayed around the edge of a bed of salad leaves. This rich sternness is followed by the killer punch that is a warm chicken mousse, slightly gelatinous in texture, the blue cheese oozing from the centre the whole dish suffused with the tastes of chicken, blue cheese and sweet butter.

Fillet of turbot has a perfect saffron cream that stripes across the plate like a splash of colour in a de Kooning canvas, whilst a following lemon and ginger sorbet impresses by virtue of the ginger flavour meaning the ice does not taste too cold.

Roast loin of lamb is sweet as Shirley Temple, a thyme jus just right, whilst marinated fruits are served slightly soupy but enjoy amazing, knockout flavours. Well-balanced, true-flavoured, sassy, excellent cooking.

Open 12.30pm-2pm, 7.30pm-9pm Mon-Sun (booking essential)
Open all year incl Xmas
Average Price: lunch £16.50, dinner £28.50
Credit Cards: Visa, Access/Mastercard, Amex, Diners
No Service Charge
Full Licence
Wheelchair Access (incl disabled bathroom)
Children — high chairs
Vegetarian meals with prior notice
The House is signposted from Rathnew, and from the main Dublin-Wicklow road, just as you enter Rathnew, on the left hand side.

THE TREE OF IDLENESS

Sea Front, Bray, Co Wicklow Tel: (01) 286 3498
Susan Courtellas

Akis Courtellas' too-early death robbed the country of a major cooking
talent, for Mr Courtellas had begun, in recent years, to both refine and
re-define the nature of Greek-Cypriot cooking, a cuisine held, for the
most part, in low regard, but which, Courtellas showed, could be raised
to heights of sublime and resonant achievement when in his hands.

Susan Courtellas has continued to run the 'Tree and, assisted by the
devoted staff who ran the show when Akis was alive, she has made the
transition smoothly.

She has also maintained the inquisitive, charged character of the
cuisine. The menu is still composed of dishes which Akis Courtellas
either created or upon which he stamped his interpretation — spinach
ravioli filled with chicken mousse and wild mushrooms with a carrot
sauce; grilled ewe's milk cheese with a tahini sauce; three fillets of beef,
lamb and veal in a mustard sauce; smoked lamb with a blackcurrant and
wine sauce — but each evening sees them beautifully re-interpreted and
delivered. We should be thankful for this, and for the expertise of the
kitchen whom Courtellas directed, for eating at the 'Tree was always one
of the great dining out experiences in Ireland and, thankfully, it remains
every bit as special today.

The great standards of the Eastern Mediterranean — Imam Bayildi,
moussaka, saddle of lamb with feta cheese and olives — are also given
an ever-new interpretation, and the food in the 'Tree can, almost
effortlessly, offer flavours that are fresh, exciting and unique. The great
dessert trolley, an Archimboldesque explosion of exotic fruits with accompanying ices and desserts, is incredible, whilst the wine list remains
deeply marvellous and rewarding.

Open 7.30pm-11pm Tue-Sat, 7.30pm-10pm Sun
Closed Xmas and two weeks in early Sept
Average Price: dinner £20
Credit Cards: Visa, Access/Mastercard, Amex, Diners
10% Service Charge
Wine Licence
Wheelchair Access (but 1 step to toilet)
Children — only with advance notice
Vegetarian dishes served each evening
The Tree Of Idleness overlooks the seafront in Bray, and is almost at the end of the
seafront.

NORTHERN IRELAND CONTENTS

ANTICA ROMA

67/69 Botanic Ave, Belfast BT7 1JL Tel: (0232) 311121 Fax: 310787
Tony Mura

The success of Antica Roma was always on the cards. Tony Mura's restaurant is part of a small group of Italian eateries in Belfast which cater, usually with unerring expertise, for different demands, different pockets and different expectations.

In other places which the family own you can get the trattoria stuff with which to fuel a Saturday night or to bring your first teenage date: pizza, pasta, Pavarotti, then some flaming sambucca. But, in Antica Roma Mr Mura has taken a deliberate step upmarket, creating an eating house whose decorations might have been borrowed from the Coliseum but were more likely adapted from a Hollywood sword'n'skirt epic (that's the men in the skirts, by the way: Kirk Douglas, Tony Quinn, perhaps Victor Mature or Richard Burton, with or without Liz).

The lavishness and enormity of the operation allows for it to get packed to the rafters at weekends with serious carousers, and this is when you see AR at its best. The food is a clever revision of standard Italian ideas and you can hit upon an excellent dinner and enjoy some of their splendid Sicilian wines, but the true ethos of the restaurant places high jinks above hâute cuisine.

You are here to enjoy yourself, not to worry about whether they have got their pesto note-perfect or their peppardelle precisely right. The people of Belfast are still not yet prepared to regard Italian food as the gloriously creative and expressive cuisine it truly is, seeing it as more serious than Indian or Chinese cooking, say, but not so serious as French. Antica Roma caters, expertly, for the desire to have food which is familiar yet still a little special, whilst not neglecting the fact that it is the right of every free born man and woman to have one hell of a good time.

Open noon-2.30pm Mon-Fri, 6pm-11pm Mon-Sat, 5pm-10pm Sun
Closed Xmas, 12 July
Average Price: dinner £25
Credit Cards: Visa, Access/Mastercard, Amex
10% Service Charge for parties of 8 or more
Full Licence
Wheelchair Access (please advise when booking)
Children — welcome
Vegetarian options always available
Half way up Botanic Avenue, just up from Shaftesbury Square.

MANOR HOUSE

47 Donegal Pass, Belfast BT7 Tel: (0232) 238755
Tony Wong

The Manor House looks just like every other Chinese restaurant in Ireland — a standard laminate-and-lacquer array of rooms with pling-plong muzak and lurid napery — and you find it in a location, directly opposite a thunderously fortified police station, which is one the most uninspiring you could possibly imagine. But, whilst you can of course opt for familiar Chinese food if you eat here, Tony Wong's restaurant does take itself more seriously than most, and the real fun only begins when you put them to their mark and bravely put yourself as close as you dare to the culinary edge.

The best advice in the Manor House is to order the unusual dishes — fish head, duck's web — and ask for them to be done in the real style, with lots of chillies and authentic seasonings. Elsewhere, this demand is usually met with a negative reply: there may be bak choi and chillies galore for the kitchen staff, but not for the punters. Here, they will actually do it for you.

Their dish of eel with roasted belly of pork, for example, presents these unlikely flavours as perfect bed fellows, the pork sticky and sweet, the eel — from Lough Neagh, and the Chinese community are just about the only folk in the North with the wisdom to buy this spectacularly fine fish — in perfect alliance with its sinuous, oily richness, the glass of Viognier in your hand proving to be the perfect complement to a bold and adventurous invention. This sort of adventure allows you to get the best from the Manor House, and to enjoy some of the most authentic and best-realised Chinese food cooked anywhere in the country. Vegetarian menus are excellent, especially with some advance notice.

Open noon-2.30pm, 5pm-11.30pm Mon-Sat
Closed Xmas, 12th & 13th July
Average Price: lunch from £5.50, dinner £10-£15
Credit Cards: Visa, Access/Mastercard, Diners
10% Service Charge
Full Licence
Wheelchair Access
Children — welcome
Full Vegetarian menu available (advance notice required)
Donegal Pass runs off Shaftesbury Square, at the bottom of Botanic Avenue.

NICK'S WAREHOUSE ➡

35/39 Hill Street, Belfast BT1 2LB Tel: (0232) 439690
Nick and Kathy Price

The Warehouse has become an institution. Unlike other institutions, however, which rapidly sink into torpor and repetition, The Warehouse re-invents itself with the mysterious calm and cunning of Dietrich or Dylan: it is someplace that is Forever Young. With the simple business of gifting you with the pleasure, delight and joy of good food in a good restaurant, there are few public places in Ireland which can compete with Nick and Kathy Price's Warehouse.

It's not just that the place is comfortable, or that the staff are very, seriously cool, in that beguiling Belfast way. It's not even that the food is exactly what you want to eat, and that it reveals such clever borrowings and influences — Anton Mosimann's Fillet of Salmon with a Vanilla Sauce, Gerry Galvin's Mussel Soup, as adapted by Mr Price himself, the Chinese inflection of Loin of Pork with Star Anise, Honey and Soy Sauce — alongside the love of punchy, zappy flavours which has made Nick Price's fortune wherever he has worked — Pigeon Breasts on Cabbage tossed in Pesto, Turbot and Lemon Sole with Tarragon Beurre Blanc, Risotto with Fennel and a Spicy Tomato Sauce.

All of this is vital, of course, but if there is something about Nick's which can truly be said to be its secret, then it is the graceful humour which Nick and Kathy bring to their work that kickstarts The Warehouse.

This is someplace which works on a theme, and the theme is whatever you want it to be. It invites you to be Devil-May-Care, at any time of the day or night. If you want to be giddy, then it's giddy. If you want to be smoochy, it's the place to smooch. If you want to enjoy serious food, then you've come to the right place. The winebar downstairs is both intimate and gregarious, the restaurant upstairs is informal and yet just right for dinner-a-deux. Who could ask for anything more?

Open noon-3.30pm Mon-Fri, 6pm-9pm Tue-Sat
Closed Xmas Day, Easter, 12th & 13th July
Average Price: lunch from £5-£18, dinner £16.95
Credit Cards: Visa, Access/Mastercard, Amex, Diners
No Service Charge (10% on parties of 6 or more)
Full Bar Licence
Wheelchair Access (disabled toilet downstairs for wine bar, lift to restaurant)
Children — in restaurant only
Recommended for Vegetarians
Hill Street is off Waring Street, just behind St. Anne's Cathedral, just down from the offices of The Belfast Telegraph, near the ring road that connects with the M2.

ROSCOFF ★ £

7 Lesley House, Shaftesbury Square, Belfast BT2 Tel: (0232) 331532
Paul and Jeanne Rankin

Following the first series of their television programme, "Gourmet Ireland", and the publication both of the accompanying book, and also the inspiring collection of recipes which is "Hot Food", Paul and Jeanne Rankin are unquestionably the most influential cooks in Ireland this century.

Their mixture of street-wise style and super-hip food has catapulted Irish cooking out of the torpor of Edwardian dining rooms and Victorian table manners, and straight into the diaspora that is up-to-the-minute world cuisine.

And they continue to create and elaborate beautiful and sensual food in the restaurant: stuffed monkfish with an anchovy and basil oil will be wrapped with the stuffing outside, all the better to preserve the fish's moist richness; a sirloin of beef with grilled leeks and a chilli butter will be such sweet surrender to the taste buds; something as simple as basil mash or a crême brûlée will knock you into smiling stupefaction.

But this perfection has been tinged, in the last year, with a modicum of inconsistency hitherto unknown in Roscoff. Occasionally, this inconsistency has been at the behest of a sense of experimentation which can seem gratuitous; sometimes it has been because the restaurant's terrifically exacting standards have not been reached. Foie Gras Won Tons might not sound like a good idea, but are glorious when successfully achieved, whilst Monkfish Tempura with a Sesame and Ginger Vinaigrette may lack the finesse the tempura demands. This period of uncertainty will pass, of course, and one looks forward to a maturing period of reflection which will fuse Mr Rankin's dynamic creativity with his passion for true flavours. In a sense the culinary adventure of Roscoff, despite its already capacious garland of awards, has only just begun.

Open 12.30pm-2pm Mon-Fri, 6.30pm-10.30pm Mon-Sat
Closed Xmas, Easter & 12 Jul
Average Price: lunch £14.50, dinner £19.50
Credit Cards: Visa, Access/Mastercard, Amex, Diners
No Service Charge
Full Licence
Full Wheelchair Access
Children — welcome, menu from £7
Recommended for Vegetarians
Right in Shaftesbury Square, on Belfast's "Golden Mile" which leads from the city centre to the university.

RAMORE

The Harbour, Portrush, Co Antrim Tel: (0265) 824313
George McAlpin

It has been the most marvellous fun, not to mention the most delicious fun, to see how The Ramore has altered its character over the last couple of years, and become a simpler, more democratic and much funkier place.

The re-invention began with a more informal dining space, the kitchen fully open to view and a set of bar chairs at the counter.

The paraphernalia of a working kitchen — the brigade of whisks, the tumbling tresses of garlic, the bottles of oil, the dog-eared texts, are all on happy exhibition along with their white-clad employers, who intersect with one another with the sure-footedness of dancers. It's a charming entertainment, as you sip aperitifs and nibble bread, but when the food arrives, it is quickly, strictly, heads-down.

For in parallel with the renovation, George McAlpin's cooking has shifted its concentration away from a convoluted French style, and has brought on board the lighter influences of the Pacific Rim.

Thus, whilst we find the signatures of foreign influence — tempura prawns with diced peppers under a trio of Mexican tostados; tagliatelle with a slurpy Roquefort sauce; char-grilled chicken with the sweetness of sun-dried tomatoes for annotation — it is just as much fun to stick with George's revisions of classic dishes, for they reveal a great sense of humour.

You can eat prawn cocktail and then steak and chips with fried onion rings here and it will be a belter of a meal: the cocktail suffuse with perfect ingredients, the steak served with onion rings so crisp and light they could be called tempura, the chips pure magic.

Chicken and duck liver parfait has a column of melba toast stored high in the style of railway sleepers, whilst exquisitely fresh fish is balanced atop a tower of perfect chips in a dazzling architectural tumbril.

The staff are super-duper and extra patient — we're afraid that it was our party which stayed 'till three a.m — the wine list short and clever — house wines are very good here — and the whole organisation devoted to delivering the best of the best times.

Open 6.30pm-10.30pm Tue-Sat (wine bar downstairs open for lunch)
Closed Xmas
Average Price: dinner £20
Credit Cards: Visa, Access/Mastercard
No Service Charge
Full Licence
Wheelchair Access to restaurant, but not to toilets
Children — controlled children welcome
Vegetarian options available with notice
Right on the harbour in Portrush, as far down the one-way system as you can drive.

DEANE'S ON THE SQUARE

Station Square, Helen's Bay, Co Down Tel: (0247) 852841/273155
Michael Deane

Michael Deane's work is unapologetically modernist, not just in what appears on the plate, but in the entire ambience which pervades Deane's On The Square.

Despite the fact that the building is a relic of Victorian days, and that it operated as a railway station house only a couple of decades ago, you are nowhere other than in the grip of the late twentieth century even before the food begins to appear.

The semi-revealed kitchen, tantalising with its glimpses of speedy work-in-progress by white-clad cooks, is a truly modern touch, showing both bravery — how many others of us would like to be overseen by an audience when we go about our work? — and also that laid-back, confident air which has become such a hallmark of restaurants in the North. These blokes are brash — a lieutenant of Mr Deane's, Raymond McArdle, was the first Northerner to qualify for the finals of the Young Chef of the Year competition in the Republic — and it shows in the food.

Michael Deane loves the pyrotechnics of preparation and elaboration, and the interplay of such signatures as a pillow of potato purée intersected with a grated potato cake, or baby scallops to sweetly offset some fine salmon, or the surprise of having the walnut component of a duck terrine placed in the dressing rather than the dish itself. There is colour too, and that distinctive sharpness of contrast which announces a cook who loves the influence of Ian McAndrew.

Best of all is the fact that Michael Deane's confidence, and the growing confidence of his kitchen, ensures an even handed expertise across the entire galaxy of food: from soup to nuts, this kitchen can deliver the goods.

Open 7pm-10pm Tue-Sat, 12.30pm-2.30pm Sun
Closed Xmas
Average Price: Sun lunch £15, dinner £19-£26
Credit Cards: Visa, Access/Mastercard, Amex
No Service Charge
Restaurant Licence
No Wheelchair Access
Children — high chairs
Vegetarian options always available
The restaurant overlooks the station platform in Helen's Bay. Look for the newly-restored tower.

THE REFECTORY
46 Mill Street, Comber, Co Down Tel: (0247) 870870
Stephen Jeffers & Michael Thomas

We might almost call it the culinary renaissance of Clandeboye. Just as Lindy Dufferin has set about the business of creating the excellent Shanks restaurant on part of the Clandeboye estate, so a pair of her former employees have opened up this fun bistro, in an upstairs series of rooms in the quiet little village of Comber.

The principal space of The Refectory is a great big, ceiling-beamed, floor-planked room, bisected by the stairs. It looks and feels like the kind of room where you come to raise quiet havoc with your friends at the weekend, but a glance at the menu will reveal that Messrs Jeffers and Thomas are serious about their work, though not so serious that they don't want you to have a good time.

When the food arrives, one is struck, again, by the flair and competence of these Northern cooks. The dishes are positively arrogant with flavour, whether a superb squid, red pepper and basil soup, served in a gargantuan bowl, or a rich and complex terrine of wild duck, pigeon and pistachios or some strips of chicken coated with sesame seeds and served with a Thai salad.

This is imaginative food, hopping all around the globe in the space of a few dishes, but it is also good fun, and even classic pairings such as cutlets of Irish lamb with haricot beans and garlic which they serve as main course doesn't kowtow to history, but gets a sprightly re-working. Best of all, perhaps, is a fine dish of baked polenta and aubergine with a smart tomato vinaigrette. Desserts, such as their special tiramisu, or a good, sharp lemon tart, are extra pleasing.

At the weekends, with the buzz of the place threatening to lift the roof, one is likely to make light work of the unpredictable service, but they need to sharpen things up somewhat on quiet nights, when the gap between courses can be a little elongated. But this is a small beer problem compared to the fine things they have already achieved.

Open 6.30pm-10pm Tue-Sat, 12.30pm-3pm Sun
Closed Xmas
Average Price: Sun lunch £12.95, dinner £19.40
Credit Cards: Visa, Access/Mastercard
No Service Charge (except parties of 8 or more, 10%)
Full Licence
No Wheelchair Access
Children — high chairs
Recommended for Vegetarians
On the main road coming in from Belfast, look for the restaurant upstairs on the right, opposite the Burma Petrol Station.

SHANKS ➥ £

The Blackwood, Crawfordsburn Rd, Bangor, Co Down Tel: (0247) 853313
Richard Gibson & Robbie Millar

Shanks was always destined to success. Put together a smart team headed by Richard Gibson, a super-confident operator, and get Robbie Millar from Roscoff as your chief cook and an ex-Ballymaloe hand like Peter Barfoot also in on the act.

Then get Terence Conran's interior design partnership, Benchmark, to design your interiors, and one might ask how you could fail?

Well, you could fail by not having sufficient ambition, despite the grandness of your surroundings, but the Shanks' team are as driven a bunch of blokes as you will find. Even in the basic business of serving a sandwich at the bar, they exhibit that meticulousness and invention which gladdens the heart. When the small things are so carefully attended to — they make the most glorious chips, for example, just brilliant — then you can relax, and tune in to enjoying the crescendo of excitement that is dinner.

Robbie Millar's food demonstrates that same drama between tension and release which has always been an integral part of Paul Rankin's cooking in Roscoff. So there are the lovely surprises of smoked garlic with a risotto of chicken livers, or truffle oil with a cod and prawn chowder. There is the same clever use of seasonal ingredients — a celeriac purée with crispy duck confit; Jerusalem artichokes with a stuffed roast chicken — and the delight in taking a straightforward dish and grabbing it by the lapels with some surprise. If some cooking is symphonic in nature — ordered, planned, predictable — then these guys are jazzers at heart — state the theme, keep the rhythm, and then raise all sorts of mayhem with it. When you get to that warm chocolate tart with pistachio ice cream, you will know these guys are blowing 'way beyond the money.

This same unpredictability is found in the organic design by Conran, daringly minimal and dashingly romantic. Some don't like it, of course. Poor old them.

Open restaurant: 12.30pm-2pm Tue-Fri, 7.30pm-10.00pm Tue-Sat; Bar and Grill: 11am-11pm Mon-Sat
Closed Xmas
Average Price: Restaurant £19.95; Bar and Grill £6
Credit Cards: Visa, Access/Mastercard   No Service Charge
Full Licence   Wheelchair Access
Children — high chairs
Vegetarian meals with prior notice
On the main Belfast/Bangor dual carriageway, take the turning for Newtownards, a few miles before Bangor. Keep following the signs for Newtownards, and you will see the signs for Shanks.

SULLIVAN'S
Sullivan Place, Holywood, Co Down Tel: (0232) 421000
Simon Shaw

Despite a modest, unassuming, patient nature — the sort of personal credentials which might normally condemn a cook to being a life-long commis in the hurly-burly of the kitchen or at best an undistinguished proprietor — Simon Shaw's restaurant has met with almost instantaneous success and, these days, everyone knows that Simon Shaw is a fine cook.

What is more, he is a fine cook with his own style and his own modest signature in his dishes. Sullivan's is Mr Shaw's first venture out on his own, after long tenures under Paul Rankin in Roscoff, just up the road in Belfast, as well as spells working in France and Switzerland and then a period when he carved interesting and enjoyable menus in Santé, just down the road from his new stomping ground. But from the day he opened up this pleasing, ambient space, he has been cooking food that is his, and his alone.

It reads predictably enough on the menu — lamb with haricots, sirloin steak, snails in a tartlette, fish of the day, duck leg with polenta, pork with red cabbage — but you find flavours here which seem that they have been teased from the dishes, so that the progress of a dinner seems beautifully sequential and, ultimately, satisfying. It seems slightly awry to suggest that Sullivan's almost has the cool ambience of a private club, but in some ways it has.

Some folk, it must be said, find the food a little understated. Certainly, if you expect fireworks every time you eat out, then Sullivan's may be too shy for your tastes. But if you relish a careful, integral simplicity in food, and enjoy solid, reassuring cooking, then these tastes can seem age-old and charmingly sedate. The fact that you can bring your own wine makes for a splendidly inexpensive evening, and makes a taxi fare within reach.

Open 10am-4pm Mon-Sat, 6.30pm-10pm Tue-Sat
Closed Xmas and bank holidays
Average Price: lunch £1.50-£7, dinner £15.50
Credit Cards: Visa, Access/Mastercard
No Service Charge, except for parties of 6 or more, 10%
No Licence (bring your own)
No Wheelchair Access
Children — half portions
Vegetarian meals always available
Sullivan's is at the top of Sullivan Place, just off Holywood town centre, near the Queen's Hall.

BEECH HILL COUNTRY HOUSE HOTEL

32 Ardmore Road, Derry, Co Londonderry Tel: (0504) 49279 Fax: 45366
Noel McMeel

The cooking in Beech Hill is the work of a shy young man named Noel
McMeel, and it is worth walking a country mile — in the rain, in the
dark — to enjoy his work. Mr McMeel's ability to traverse that danger
zone wherein a cook must accommodate the somewhat conservative
nature of his customers and, at the same time, create food which inspires
his own creativity, is one of the most delicious resolutions in the world
of Irish food.

Deliciousness, indeed, is his hallmark. The intricate techniques
which he so confidently masters — topping some local salmon with foie
gras and setting the lot on a spaghetti of cucumber and a champagne
butter sauce; serving pan-fried pork with tomato noodles and a basil
sauce — are secondary to his love of flavour. You can eat dishes in the
Beech Hill which are more than just spoon lickin' and finger lickin': this
is plate lickin' stuff.

With things that are timeworn and, for others, uninspiring, McMeel
achieves a crescendo of tastes and a synthesis of food cultures that has
delight jumping out of every dish: fillet of beef has delightful horseradish
dumplings and a rich cep and thyme jus; medallions of monkfish are
jizzed up with a ginger, fresh coriander and sesame vinaigrette and
served with fresh pasta; venison is perfectly partnered with a Sloe gin
and bramble sauce and a tense raspberry chutney.

However he does manage it, his ability to combine trusted favourite
tastes with excursions into modern improvisations is nothing but a joy
and, with increased experience, McMeel has begun to sign dishes with his
own signature. Mr McMeel could rest on his laurels, even at his tender
age, and be regarded as one of the most distinctive and intelligent cooks in
Ireland. But, he is off travelling for the early part of this year, having won
a scholarship to the United States. One awaits his return in June, armed
with the fruit of new experience, with bated breath, and bated appetite.

Open noon-2.30pm, 6pm-9.45pm Mon-Sun
Closed 24–25 Dec
Average Price: lunch from £11.50, dinner from £17.95
Credit Cards: Visa, Access/Mastercard, Amex
No Service Charge
Full Licence
Wheelchair Access (but 1 step to toilet)
Children — high chairs and half portions
Recommended for Vegetarians
Beech Hill is signposted from the A2, just past Drumahoe as you come into Derry on
the main Belfast road.

The Serious Matter of Beer

MIDNIGHT IN A LA MORTE SUBITE, in the centre of Brussels. A convocation of youthful Belgians — Levis, loafers, Sisley-separates, the bequeathed uniform of the European working classes — are noisily doing their national service, pleasingly working their way through an evening's portion of the 120 litres of beer which they drink annually.

Round about this woozy hour, with a glass of mellow, dark Faro beer in your hand, this gorgeous pub can seem ill-named, for the concatenation of the glorious beers, and the ill-disguised pride with which they are served and drunk, means you tumble into slow pleasure rather than sudden death.

Another bottle of cherry-rich Kriek, or a vintage Chimay from the Trappist monastery of Abbaye de Scourmont, or a distinctively sharp glass of Stella Artois, and you might well kick off your shoes, settle in for the night, and decide not to return home from this paradise of beer.

"Belgium has the most diverse, individualistic brews in the world", writes Michael Jackson, that guru of all things topped with froth. "The Belgians like to talk about beer as their reply to Burgundy. They suggest that beer is to them what wine is to France".

This is not merely a nationalistic remark, however, for the similarities and comparisons between the practices and techniques of wine-making and brewing are remarkable.

"Wines begin with fruit (usually, but not always, the grape), while beers start with grain (customarily, but not necessarily, barley); both are made by fermentation; and many of the flavour compounds naturally formed are shared between them. Distil wine and you have brandy. Distil beer and you make whisky."

It is this complexity, this richness, which our vaguely snobbish dismissal of beer as not being a "serious" drink overlooks. Honed and reared as we are to see beer as something which a man behind a counter pours in to a pint glass which we then empty, before doing the same thing all over again, we "fail to understand that there are different brews for each mood, moment and purpose", says Mr Jackson. Irish pubs may be the greatest in the world, but the slow attrition of variety amongst our own brews has left us with a trio of stouts and a clatter of lagers which are all too similar.

In addition, as pubs have increasingly devoted more space and time to food, the care and attention which should be devoted to handling glasses properly has declined. The culture with which we surround the sacred pint in Ireland has, all too often, too much to do with quantity, and not enough to do with quality.

Such bliss it is, then, in A la Morte Subite and in every other Belgium bar, to find that each beer has its own type of glass — the raspberry beer, Framboise, in a flute; the cherry-flavoured Kriek in a cherry-shaped balloon glass; a Pilsener-style lager such as Stella in a thin, tall glass; a dark Faro in a voluptuous orb of a glass that reminds one of a brandy balloon.

Beer is a sensual drink, its sensuality bound up in the fact that it refreshes whilst at the same time offering scents and aromas and tastes which are every bit as complex as those we might find in a good glass of wine. This sensuality needs to be taken seriously, so the correct glass and the correct temperature are of vital importance. Put this trinity of ingredients together, and it is then that we hit upon the ultimate summer drink at its best.

Brewers need grains to begin their work. Barley is the optimum choice, but wheat, oats and rye can all be malted, the first process in the making of beer. Whilst one needs only to squeeze grapes to extract their juice, grains must first be steeped and then allowed to germinate, before they are dried. The barley has now become malt.

In a huge brewery like the Stella Artois plant, in Louvain, half an hour from Brussels, one can peer along a gigantic floor 200 metres long with forty tons of barley being malted, a process which begins here with French summer barley which is steeped for three days, then germinated on the floor for between 4 to 6 days. The malt is then dried and then mashed — mixed with hot water — before being drained off.

The next process is to mix the juices of the malt with hops, in order to impart aroma and the necessary bitterness which makes a beer refreshing. In the Stella brewery they use Saaz hops, grown around the town of Zatec in Bohemia, for the bitterness they impart, as well as hops from Yugoslavia and Germany, whilst in the Belle-Vue Brewery, in the centre of Brussels, they use English hops. The hops, juice and water are then fermented with yeasts, and it is here that one encounters one of the most exciting variables in brewing.

The Belle-Vue brewery makes beers which are known as Lambics. "It is the use of wild yeasts that gives such a vinous aroma and palate (reminiscent of fino sherry, or vermouth) to the lambic family of beers", writes Michael Jackson. "No other style of beer in the developed world is intentionally made with wild strains as the principal yeasts, and it is this procedure, which occurs spontaneously, which defines a lambic. All beer — and wine — was once made in this way, with the wild yeasts producing a slightly different result each time".

In Belle-Vue, they will tell you that "you can't ever make the same lambic — it's impossible!". Using wild yeasts to invoke spontaneous fermentation involves the law of the jungle, but the results of this crazy process makes for a beer which is startlingly refreshing: on a hot day there is nothing like a Geuze — a blending of young and old lambics — for slaking a thirst, its clean cut of flavour annointed at the back of the mouth with the busy complexity of bitter hop flavours.

Preserving an environment which suits wild yeasts means that the cellars of the Belle-Vue brewery, with their warrens of massive oak casks, are littered with cobwebs. It is a marvellously artisan, timeless place and their specialist beers — the cherry-flavoured Kriek, the raspberry-flavoured Framboise — are ruddy, refreshing, pure drinks.

In Louvain, meanwhile, the Stella Artois brewery not only shows the modern side of brewing — the plant is spectacularly modern, with the centrepiece of the production being a maze of 24 computer screens

which keep tabs on the continuous brewing process — but also the modern use of cultivated yeasts. For Pilsner-style lager beers use laboratory yeasts, the first variety of which was only isolated in 1883. These yeasts ferment at the bottom of the vat, working slowly at colder temperatures than those yeasts which ferment at the top of the vat, and thus give a cleaner, clearer, more rounded character.

Stella is a defining example of the sourness and sharpness which a good Pilsner-style lager should offer: without the slight note of sourness a beer cannot be refreshing, and the spicy, mineral quality of the beer is delicious. You can't drink it without wanting a dish of marinated herring, or even just a plate of crisp chips for, like any good beer, it suits food perfectly.

Beer, that sensual drink, rewards savouring and appreciating every bit as much as wine. Dip a toe into the pool and you find quickly that you become sensitive to the use of the hops, or the fact that Lambic beers must have a minimum of 30% of wheat used along with the barley, or the subtle nuttiness of English ale.

The division of styles and the use of skills in brewing soon becomes as important and as valuable as discovering which grape varieties you prefer, and the advent of beer language, with its similarity to wine-speak, follows: notes of juniper; nutmeg; mineral elements; toast; butter; apricots, you name it.

The idea of always drinking the same beer, irrespective of which pub you are in or whatever it is you are doing at home, soon becomes an absurd idea. You would never drink the same glass of wine, irrespective of where you were and the day that was in it, so why always order the same beer? Similarly, being uninquisitive about beer, on the grounds, presumably, that all beers are all much of a muchness, is crazy. "No one goes into a restaurant and requests 'a plate of food please'", writes Michael Jackson.

"People do not ask simply for 'a glass of wine' without specifying, at the very least, whether they fancy red or white, dry or sweet, perhaps sparkling or still". Yet, he points out, "When their mood switches from the grape to the grain, these same discerning folk often ask simply for 'a beer', or perhaps name a brand, without thinking about its suitability for the mood or moment".

Beer is a rich and worthy subject which, hopefully, will soon blossom out, in Ireland, from the stranglehold of the big brewers as we see the advent of micro-breweries and dedicated folk making specialist beers. The effect of the homogenisation of the beer market has been to close our eyes to the vast variety of the subject. But, just spend a couple of days in Brussels, touring through the Belle-Vue brewery, or letting a glass of Lambic sink you into comfortable slothfulness in A la Morte Subite or Le Roy D'Espagne on the Grand Place, and a panorama opens up, a vista of bibulous pleasure.

Index

CHEERS

OTHER TITLES FROM ESTRAGON PRESS

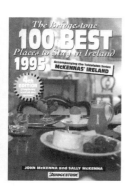

The Bridgestone Irish Food Guide

André Simon Special Award-winning Bridgestone Irish Food Guide is the most comprehensive, independent, critical guide to the very best food in Ireland. From the most committed and creative artisan food producers north and south to the finest restaurants east and west, the Bridgestone Irish Food Guide explores and describes in extensive detail Ireland's inspiring, blossoming food culture. Price: £11.99

The Bridgestone 100 Best Places to Stay in Ireland

From simple B&Bs to grand Country Houses, from welcoming Farmhouses to luxurious Hotels, this book finds the best places to stay in Ireland. Price: £5.99

The Bridgestone 100 Best Places to Eat in Dublin

The definitive critical independent guide to the finest meals in Dublin, from pizzerias to the grandest restaurants. Simply the essential guide to the capital city's best food. Price: £5.99

The Bridgestone Vegetarian's Guide to Ireland

A comprehensive guide for vegetarians to the finest Irish vegetarian food, written in the style of the award-winning Bridgestone Irish Food Guide. Covering every possible food source, from farms and shops through to restaurants and the best accommodation, this is the definitive guide for vegetarians. Price: £6.99

SO! WHO BRINGS CHEF THE LAST ORDER?.